SPORTY'

WHAT YOU SHOULD KNOW™ SERIES
PTS STUDY GUIDE

Private Pilot
Practical Test Standards
for
Airplane Single-Engine Land
Cross-Referenced
to
Sporty's Interactive DVD Course

Sporty's Academy, Inc.
Clermont County/Sporty's Airport
Batavia, OH 45103

For additional copies, reorder #M116A

Call: 1 (USA) 800.SPORTYS
(776.7897)

Fax: 1 (USA) 800.359.7794
1 (USA) 513.735.9200
sportys.com

05/06

Page Intentionally Left Blank

Table of Contents

Preface iv

Conventions Used in This Manual v

FAA References Used in This Manual.. v

Section 1 - Private Pilot Practical Test Standards for Airplane Single-Engine Land with DVD
       Cross-Reference 1-1

I.   **Area Of Operation: Preflight Preparation** **1-1**
       A.   Task: Certificates And Documents (ASEL and ASES) _____ 1-1
       B.   Task: Airworthiness Requirements (ASEL and ASES) _____ 1-1
       C.   Task: Weather Information (ASEL and ASES) _____ 1-1
       D.   Task: Cross-Country Flight Planning (ASEL and ASES) _____ 1-1
       E.   Task: National Airspace System (ASEL and ASES) _____ 1-2
       F.   Task: Performance And Limitations (ASEL and ASES) _____ 1-2
       G.   Task: Operation Of Systems (ASEL and ASES) _____ 1-2
       H.   Task: Water And Seaplane Characteristics (ASES) _____ 1-2
       I.   Task: Seaplane Bases, Maritime Rules, And Aids To Marine Navigation (ASES) _____ 1-2
       J.   Task: Aeromedical Factors (ASEL and ASES) _____ 1-3

II.   **Area Of Operation: Preflight Procedures** **1-4**
       A.   Task: Preflight Inspection (ASEL and ASES) _____ 1-4
       B.   Task: Cockpit Management (ASEL and ASES) _____ 1-4
       C.   Task: Engine Starting (ASEL and ASES)_____ 1-4
       D.   Task: Taxiing (ASEL and ASES) _____ 1-4
       E.   Task: Taxiing And Sailing (ASES)_____ 1-4
       F.   Task: Before Takeoff Check (ASEL and ASES) _____ 1-4

III.   **Area Of Operation: Airport And Seaplane Base Operations** **1-5**
       A.   Task: Radio Communications And ATC Light Signals (ASEL and ASES) _____ 1-5
       B.   Task: Traffic Patterns (ASEL and ASES)_____ 1-5
       C.   Task: Airport/Seaplane Base, Runway, and Taxiway Signs, Markings, And Lighting (ASEL and ASES)_ 1-5

IV.   **Area Of Operation: Takeoffs, Landings, And Go-Arounds** **1-6**
       A.   Task: Normal And Crosswind Takeoff And Climb (ASEL and ASES)_____ 1-6
       B.   Task: Normal And Crosswind Approach And Landing (ASEL and ASES) _____ 1-6
       C.   Task: Soft-Field Takeoff And Climb (ASEL) _____ 1-6
       D.   Task: Soft-Field Approach And Landing (ASEL) _____ 1-7
       E.   Task: Short-Field Takeoff (Confined Area-ASES) And Maximum Performance Climb (ASEL and ASES)1-7
       F.   Task: Short-Field Approach (Confined Area-ASES) And Landing (ASEL and ASES) _____ 1-7
       G.   Task: Glassy Water Takeoff And Climb (ASES) _____ 1-8
       H.   Task: Glassy Water Approach And Landing (ASES)_____ 1-8
       I.   Task: Rough Water Takeoff And Climb (ASES) _____ 1-8
       J.   Task: Rough Water Approach And Landing (ASES)_____ 1-8
       K.   Task: Forward Slip To A Landing (ASEL and ASES)_____ 1-9
       L.   Task: Go-Around/Rejected Landing (ASEL and ASES) _____ 1-9

V.   **Area Of Operation: Performance Maneuver** **1-10**
       A.   Task: Steep Turns (ASEL and ASES) _____ 1-10

VI.   **Area Of Operation: Ground Reference Maneuvers** **1-11**
       A.   Task: Rectangular Course (ASEL and ASES) _____ 1-11
       B.   Task: S-Turns (ASEL and ASES)_____ 1-11
       C.   Task: Turns Around A Point (ASEL and ASES) _____ 1-11

VII.   Area Of Operation: Navigation **1-12**
   A.   Task: Pilotage And Dead Reckoning (ASEL and ASES) _____ 1-12
   B.   Task: Navigation Systems And Radar Services (ASEL and ASES) _____ 1-12
   C.   Task: Diversion (ASEL and ASES) _____ 1-12
   D.   Task: Lost Procedures (ASEL and ASES) _____ 1-12

VIII. Area Of Operation: Slow Flight And Stalls **1-13**
   A.   Task: Maneuvering During Slow Flight (ASEL and ASES) _____ 1-13
   B.   Task: Power-Off Stalls (ASEL and ASES) _____ 1-13
   C.   Task: Power-On Stalls (ASEL and ASES) _____ 1-13
   D.   Task: Spin Awareness (ASEL and ASES) _____ 1-13

IX.   Area Of Operation: Basic Instrument Maneuvers **1-14**
   A.   Task: Straight-And-Level Flight (ASEL and ASES) _____ 1-14
   B.   Task: Constant Airspeed Climbs (ASEL and ASES) _____ 1-14
   C.   Task: Constant Airspeed Descents (ASEL and ASES) _____ 1-14
   D.   Task: Turns To Headings (ASEL and ASES)_____ 1-14
   E.   Task: Recovery From Unusual Flight Attitudes (ASEL and ASES) _____ 1-14
   F.   Task: Radio Communications, Navigation Systems/Facilities, And Radar Services (ASEL and ASES) _ 1-14

X.   Area Of Operation: Emergency Operations **1-15**
   A.   Task: Emergency Approach And Landing (ASEL and ASES) _____ 1-15
   B.   Task: Systems And Equipment Malfunctions (ASEL and ASES) _____ 1-15
   C.   Task: Emergency Equipment And Survival Gear (ASEL and ASES) _____ 1-15

XI.   Area Of Operation: Night Operations **1-16**
   A.   Task: Night Preparation (ASEL and ASES)_____ 1-16

XII.   Area Of Operation: Postflight Procedures **1-17**
   A.   Task: After Landing, Parking, And Securing (ASEL and ASES) _____ 1-17
   B.   Task: Anchoring (ASES) _____ 1-17
   C.   Task: Docking And Mooring (ASES)_____ 1-17
   D.   Task: Ramping/Beaching (ASES) _____ 1-17

Supplemental PTS Information **1-18**
   Practical Test Standards Description_____ 1-18
   Use of the Practical Test Standards Book _____ 1-18
   Special Emphasis Areas _____ 1-19
   Private Pilot - Airplane Practical Test Prerequisites _____ 1-19
   Aircraft and Equipment Required for the Practical Test_____ 1-19
   Flight Instructor Responsibility_____ 1-20
   Examiner Responsibility _____ 1-20
   Satisfactory Performance _____ 1-20
   Unsatisfactory Performance _____ 1-21
   Crew Resource Management (CRM) _____ 1-21
   Applicant's Use of Checklists_____ 1-21
   Use of Distractions During Practical Tests _____ 1-21
   Positive Exchange of Flight Controls _____ 1-21
   Metric Conversion Initiative _____ 1-22
   Additional Rating Task Table – Airplane Single-Engine Land _____ 1-22
   Applicant's Practical Test Checklist_____ 1-23
   Examiner's Practical Test Checklist _____ 1-24

Section 2 - Private Pilot DVD Study Guide *2-1*

Volume 1 - Your First Few Hours 2-1
Aerodynamics _____ 2-1
Engines/Preflight _____ 2-2
Federal Aviation Regulations _____ 2-2

Volume 2 - Practicing Landings 2-3
Engines/Preflight _____ 2-3
Aerodynamics _____ 2-3

Volume 3 - Your First Solo 2-4
Aerodynamics _____ 2-4
Weather Theory _____ 2-4
Weather Data _____ 2-4
Aircraft Instruments _____ 2-6
Aeromedical _____ 2-6
Federal Aviation Regulations _____ 2-6
Collision Avoidance _____ 2-6

Volume 5 - Your Dual Cross-Countries 2-7
Airport Lighting & Marking _____ 2-7
Collision Avoidance _____ 2-7
Publications _____ 2-7
Navigation _____ 2-7
VOR Navigation _____ 2-8
ADF Navigation _____ 2-8
Weather Data _____ 2-9
Airspace _____ 2-9

Volume 6 - Your Solo Cross-Countries 2-12
Aircraft Performance _____ 2-12
Weather Theory _____ 2-12

Volume 7 - Your Private Pilot Test 2-13
Federal Aviation Regulations _____ 2-13

Section 3 - Appendices and Supplemental Material *3-1*

Appendix A – Airworthiness Requirements for VFR Flight 3-1

Appendix B – Additional Weather Information 3-3

Appendix C – Motion Sickness and Dehydration 3-15

Appendix D – Securing Loose Items 3-15

Appendix E – Noise Abatement Procedures 3-16

Appendix F – Determining Minimum Safe Altitude for Emergency Instrument Navigation 3-16

Appendix G – Emergency and Survival Equipment 3-17

Appendix H – Instructor Certification for Private Pilot Knowledge Test 3-17

Preface

Sporty's *What You Should Know*™ Complete Flight Training DVD course has been designed to completely prepare you to become a Private Pilot.

The subject matter is presented in a logical sequence that parallels the flight instruction you will be receiving. This sequence is also the best way to prepare for the FAA computerized knowledge exam. This book is not a substitute for the DVDs, but a supplement to help you prepare more completely for your knowledge test, oral and practical exams, and to become a better pilot.

This study guide is arranged into two major sections.

The first section contains the Private Pilot Practical Test Standards for Airplane Single-Engine with a DVD cross-reference. This section is intended to be used as a review prior to your oral and practical exams. It also may be used as a supplemental index to the DVDs. It relates the various elements of the PTS to the appropriate Sporty's DVD volumes and segments for further review. The test standards for both land and sea airplanes are included for completeness. The cross-reference to the DVD is only included for Single-Engine Land elements. Tasks and elements specific to Single-Engine Sea airplanes are labeled as ASES Only.

The second section contains supplemental material that you should study after watching each DVD volume. This information will support the subjects presented by the related DVDs and will provide reinforcing notes or may be used as a quick reference.

This study guide *is not* intended to stand alone. It is a part of the total training package supplied with Sporty's *What You Should Know* Complete Flight Training DVD course.

Best of luck with your studies and welcome to your new adventure.

Sporty's Academy, Staff
May, 2006
Batavia, Ohio

Conventions Used in This Manual

The Private Pilot Practical Test Standards (PTS) with DVD Cross-Reference contains the text of the PTS with references to information that may be found in Sporty's *Complete* Flight Training Course DVDs for each element. The cross-reference will appear in the following format:
➤ A number indicating the DVD volume will be followed by a period and number indicating the segment within the DVD. For example, 5.1 would indicate to refer to Segment 1 of DVD Volume 5 from the course.

Appendices and pages within this study guide and the AFM/POH for your airplane are also referenced.

The PTS includes tasks and elements which are specific to both the Airplane Single-Engine Land (ASEL) and the Airplane Single-Engine Sea (ASES) ratings. The information for both is included for completeness, but the items specific to the ASES rating are not cross-referenced.

FAA References Used in This Manual

Many of the references below were used by the FAA in preparing the PTS. Most of the references listed are books and may be purchased from Sporty's by calling 1.800.SPORTYS (776.7897) from the USA or by logging on to sportys.com.

14 CFR Part 43 Maintenance, Preventive Maintenance, Rebuilding, and Alteration
14 CFR Part 61 Certification: Pilots and Flight Instructors
14 CFR Part 91 General Operating and Flight Rules
NTSB Part 830 Notification and Reporting of Aircraft Accidents and Incidents
FAA-H-8083-1 Aircraft Weight and Balance Handbook
FAA-H-8083-3 Airplane Flying Handbook
FAA-H-8083-15 Instrument Flying Handbook
FAA-H-8083-25 Pilot's Handbook of Aeronautical Knowledge
AC 00-2 Advisory Circular Checklist
AC 00-6 Aviation Weather
AC 00-45 Aviation Weather Services
AC 61-65 Certification: Pilots and Flight Instructors
AC 61-67 Stall Spin Awareness Training
AC 61-84 Role of Preflight Preparation
AC 65-12 Airframe and Powerplant Mechanics Powerplant Handbook
AC 65-15 Airframe and Powerplant Mechanics Airframe Handbook
AC 67-2 Medical Handbook for Pilots
AC 90-48 Pilots' Role in Collision Avoidance
AC 120-51 Crew Resource Management Training
AIM Aeronautical Information Manual
A/FD Airport/Facility Directory
NOTAMs Notices to Airmen
AFM/POH - FAA-Approved Flight Manual/Pilot Operating Handbook

Page Intentionally Left Blank

Section 1 - Private Pilot Practical Test Standards for Airplane Single-Engine Land with DVD Cross-Reference

I.   AREA OF OPERATION: PREFLIGHT PREPARATION

NOTE: The examiner shall develop a scenario based on real time weather to evaluate TASKs C and D.

A.   TASK: CERTIFICATES AND DOCUMENTS (ASEL AND ASES)

Objective: To determine that the applicant exhibits knowledge of the elements related to certificates and documents by:

DVD Volume.Segment

1. Explaining-
   a) pilot certificate, privileges, limitations, and recent flight experience requirements. 7.1
   b) medical certificate, class and duration. 3.22, 7.1
   c) pilot logbook or flight records. 7.1
2. Locating and explaining-
   a) airworthiness and registration certificates. 1.13, 7.1
   b) operating limitations, placards, instrument markings, handbooks, and POH/AFM 1.13, 7.1
   c) weight and balance data and equipment list. 3.18, 7.6, 7.7

B.   TASK: AIRWORTHINESS REQUIREMENTS (ASEL AND ASES)

Objective: To determine that the applicant exhibits knowledge of the elements related to airworthiness requirements by:

1. Explaining-
   a) required instruments and equipment for day/night VFR. ....Appendix A
   b) procedures and limitations for determining airworthiness of the airplane with inoperative instruments and equipment with and without an MEL. ....Appendix A
   c) requirements and procedures for obtaining a special flight permit. ....Appendix A
2. Locating and explaining-
   a) airworthiness directives. ....Appendix A
   b) compliance records. 7.1
   c) maintenance/inspection requirements. 7.1
   d) appropriate record keeping. 7.1

C.   TASK: WEATHER INFORMATION (ASEL AND ASES)

Objective: To determine that the applicant:

1. Exhibits knowledge of the elements related to weather information by analyzing weather reports, charts, and forecasts from various sources with emphasis on- 3.1, 3.9, 3.11, 3.12, 5.12, 5.13, 6.12
   a) METAR, TAF, and FA. 3.11, 5.13
   b) surface analysis chart. ....Appendix B
   c) radar summary chart. 3.11
   d) winds and temperature aloft chart. ....Appendix B
   e) significant weather prognostic charts. 5.13
   f) convective outlook chart. 6.12
   g) AWOS, ASOS, and ATIS reports. 6.1, 6.12
2. Makes a competent "go/no-go" decision based on available weather information. 1.2, 6.16

D.   TASK: CROSS-COUNTRY FLIGHT PLANNING (ASEL AND ASES)

Objective: To determine that the applicant:

1. Exhibits knowledge of the elements related to cross-country flight planning by presenting and explaining a preplanned VFR cross-country flight, as previously assigned by the examiner. On the day of the practical test, the final flight plan shall be to the first fuel stop, based on maximum allowable passengers, baggage, and/or cargo loads using real-time weather. 5.All, 6.All
2. Uses appropriate, current aeronautical charts. 5.3
3. Properly identifies airspace, obstructions, and terrain features. 5.3, 5.17
4. Selects easily identifiable en route checkpoints. 5.3, 5.5
5. Selects the most favorable altitudes considering weather conditions and equipment capabilities. 5.3, 6.9
6. Computes headings, flight time, and fuel requirements. 5.5, 5.6, 5.16, 6.9
7. Selects appropriate navigation systems/facilities and communication frequencies. 5.5, 5.7, 5.8, 5.9
8. Applies pertinent information from NOTAMs, the A/FD, and other flight publications. 5.3
9. Completes a navigation log and simulates filing a VFR flight plan. 5.5, 5.15, 7.4, 7.8

E. **Task: National Airspace System (ASEL and ASES)**

Objective: To determine that the applicant exhibits knowledge of the elements related to the National Airspace System by explaining:

1. Basic VFR Weather Minimums - for all classes of airspace. ....5.17, PTS Study Guide Page 2-11
2. Airspace classes - their operating rules, pilot certification, and airplane equipment requirements for the following-
   a) Class A. ....5.17, PTS Study Guide Page 2-11
   b) Class B. ....5.17, PTS Study Guide Page 2-11
   c) Class C. ....5.17, PTS Study Guide Page 2-11
   d) Class D. ....5.17, PTS Study Guide Page 2-11
   e) Class E. ....5.17, PTS Study Guide Page 2-11
   f) Class G. ....5.17, PTS Study Guide Page 2-11
3. Special use airspace and other airspace areas. ....5.17, PTS Study Guide Page 2-9

F. **Task: Performance And Limitations (ASEL and ASES)**

Objective: To determine that the applicant:

1. Exhibits knowledge of the elements related to performance and limitations by explaining the use of charts, tables, and data to determine performance and the adverse effects of exceeding limitations. 3.18, 6.5, 7.6, 7.7
2. Computes weight and balance. Determines the computed weight and center of gravity is within the airplane's operating limitations and if the weight and center of gravity will remain within limits during all phases of flight. 3.18, 7.6, 7.7
3. Demonstrates use of the appropriate performance charts, tables, and data 6.5, 7.6
4. Describes the effects of atmospheric conditions on the airplane's performance. 2.3, 3.7, 3.8, 6.5

G. **Task: Operation Of Systems (ASEL and ASES)**

Objective: To determine that the applicant exhibits knowledge of the elements related to the operation of systems on the airplane provided for the flight test by explaining at least three of the following:

1. Primary flight controls and trim. 1.4
2. Flaps, leading edge devices, and spoilers. 1.4, 1.6
3. Water rudders (ASES). ....ASES Only
4. Powerplant and Propeller. 1.1, 1.6, 1.7, 1.8, 2.3
5. Landing gear. ....AFM/POH
6. Fuel, oil, and hydraulic systems. 1.1, 1.8
7. Electrical. 1.1
8. Avionics. 1.23, 5.7, 5.8, 5.9
9. Pitot-static, vacuum/pressure, and associated flight instruments. 1.6, 2.6, 3.7, 3.13
10. Environmental. ....AFM/POH
11. Deicing and anti-icing. 1.11

H. **Task: Water And Seaplane Characteristics (ASES)**

Objective: To determine that the applicant exhibits knowledge of the elements related to water and seaplane characteristics by explaining:

1. The characteristics of a water surface as affected by features, such as-
   a) size and location. ....ASES Only
   b) protected and unprotected areas. ....ASES Only
   c) surface wind. ....ASES Only
   d) direction and strength of water current. ....ASES Only
   e) floating and partially submerged debris. ....ASES Only
   f) sandbars, islands, and shoals. ....ASES Only
   g) vessel traffic and wakes. ....ASES Only
   h) other features peculiar to the area. ....ASES Only
2. Float and hull construction, and their effect on seaplane performance. ....ASES Only
3. Causes of porpoising and skipping, and the pilot action required to prevent or correct these occurrences. ....ASES Only

I. **Task: Seaplane Bases, Maritime Rules, And Aids To Marine Navigation (ASES)**

Objective: To determine that the applicant exhibits knowledge of the elements related to seaplane bases, maritime rules, and aids to marine navigation by explaining:

1. How to locate and identify seaplane bases on charts or in directories. ....ASES Only
2. Operating restrictions at various bases. ....ASES Only
3. Right-of-way, steering, and sailing rules pertinent to seaplane operation. ....ASES Only
4. Marine navigation aids such as buoys, beacons, lights, and sound signals. ....ASES Only

J.   TASK: AEROMEDICAL FACTORS (ASEL AND ASES)

Objective: To determine that the applicant exhibits knowledge of the elements related to aeromedical factors by explaining:

**DVD
Volume.Segment**

1.   The symptoms, causes, effects, and corrective actions of at least three (3) of the following-
    a)   hypoxia...3.22
    b)   hyperventilation. 3.22
    c)   middle ear and sinus problems...3.23
    d)   spatial disorientation. 3.22
    e)   motion sickness... Appendix C
    f)   carbon monoxide poisoning..3.22
    g)   stress and fatigue..3.23
    h)   dehydration. .... Appendix C
2.   The effects of alcohol and over-the-counter drugs. 3.23, 7.1
3.   The effects of nitrogen excesses during scuba dives upon a pilot or passenger in flight. 7.8

II.   AREA OF OPERATION: PREFLIGHT PROCEDURES

A.   TASK: PREFLIGHT INSPECTION (ASEL AND ASES)

Objective: To determine that the applicant:

DVD
Volume.Segment

1.   Exhibits knowledge of the elements related to preflight inspection. This shall include which items must be inspected, the reasons for checking each item, and how to detect possible defects..1.13, 7.10
2.   Inspects the airplane with reference to the checklist. ....1.13, AFM/POH
3.   Verifies the airplane is in condition for safe flight. 1.12, 1.13

B.   TASK: COCKPIT MANAGEMENT (ASEL AND ASES)

Objective: To determine that the applicant:

1.   Exhibits knowledge of the elements related to cockpit management procedures. 7.10
2.   Ensures all loose items in the cockpit and cabin are secured. ....Appendix D
3.   Organizes material and equipment in an efficient manner so they are readily available. 7.10
4.   Briefs occcupants on the use of safety belts, shoulder harnesses, doors, and emergency procedures. 1.14, 7.10

C.   TASK: ENGINE STARTING (ASEL AND ASES)

Objective: To determine that the applicant:

1.   Exhibits knowledge of the elements related to recommended engine starting procedures. This shall include the use of an external power source, hand propping safety, and starting under various atmospheric conditions. 1.14, 7.10
2.   Positions the airplane properly considering structures, surface conditions, other aircraft, and the safety of nearby persons and property. 1.14
3.   Utilizes the appropriate checklist for starting procedure. ....1.14, AFM/POH

D.   TASK: TAXIING (ASEL AND ASES)

Objective: To determine that the applicant:

1.   Exhibits knowledge of the elements related to safe taxi procedures. 1.17, 7.10
2.   Performs a brake check immediately after the airplane begins moving. 1.17
3.   Positions the flight controls properly for the existing wind conditions. 1.17, 1.18, 7.10
4.   Controls direction and speed without excessive use of brakes. 1.17, 7.10
5.   Complies with airport/taxiway markings, signals, ATC clearances, and instructions..3.15
6.   Taxies so as to avoid other aircraft and hazards. 1.17, 7.10

E.   TASK: TAXIING AND SAILING (ASES)

Objective: To determine that the applicant:

1.   Exhibits knowledge of the elements related to water taxi and sailing procedures. ....ASES Only
2.   Positions the flight controls properly for the existing wind conditions. ....ASES Only
3.   Plans and follows the most favorable course while taxi or sailing considering wind, water current, water conditions and maritime regulations. ....ASES Only
4.   Uses the appropriate idle, plow, or step taxi technique. ....ASES Only
5.   Uses flight controls, flaps, doors, water rudder, and power correctly so as to follow the desired course while sailing. ....ASES Only
6.   Prevents and corrects for porpoising and skipping..ASES Only
7.   Avoids other aircraft, vessels, and hazards..ASES Only
8.   Complies with seaplane base signs, signals, and clearances. ....ASES Only

F.   TASK: BEFORE TAKEOFF CHECK (ASEL AND ASES)

Objective: To determine that the applicant:

1.   Exhibits knowledge of the elements related to the before takeoff check. This shall include the reasons for checking each item and how to detect malfunctions...1.17, 7.10
2.   Positions the airplane properly considering other aircraft/vessels, wind and surface conditions....................................1.17
3.   Divides attention inside and outside the cockpit...7.10
4.   Ensures that engine temperature and pressure are suitable for run-up and takeoff. ....AFM/POH
5.   Accomplishes the before takeoff check and ensures the airplane is in safe operating condition. 1.17
6.   Reviews takeoff performance airspeeds, takeoff distances, departure, and emergency procedures. 7.10
7.   Avoids runway incursions and/or ensures no conflict with traffic prior to taxiing into takeoff position....................1.19, 1.21

III.   AREA OF OPERATION: AIRPORT AND SEAPLANE BASE OPERATIONS

DVD
Volume.Segment

A.   TASK: RADIO COMMUNICATIONS AND ATC LIGHT SIGNALS (ASEL AND ASES)

Objective: To determine that the applicant:

1.   Exhibits knowledge of the elements related to radio communications and ATC light signals. 1.15, 3.20, 6.1
2.   Selects appropriate frequencies..6.1, 7.14
3.   Transmits using recommended phraseology...1.15, 1.16, 1.20, 3.19, 6.1, 7.10
4.   Acknowledges radio communications and complies with instructions. 1.15, 1.20, 6.1

B.   TASK: TRAFFIC PATTERNS (ASEL AND ASES)

Objective: To determine that the applicant:

1.   Exhibits knowledge of the elements related to traffic patterns. This shall include procedures at airports with and without operating control towers, prevention of runway incursions, collision avoidance, wake turbulence avoidance, and wind shear..1.17, 2.11, 2.13, 7.10
2.   Complies with proper traffic pattern procedures. 1.17, 2.11
3.   Maintains proper spacing from other traffic. 7.10
4.   Corrects for wind drift to maintain the proper ground track...2.1, 2.11, 2.13
5.   Maintains orientation with the runway/landing area in use. 2.11
6.   Maintains traffic pattern altitude, ±100 feet (30 meters), and the appropriate airspeed, ±10 knots.................................7.10

C.   TASK: AIRPORT/SEAPLANE BASE, RUNWAY, AND TAXIWAY SIGNS, MARKINGS, AND LIGHTING (ASEL AND ASES)

Objective: To determine that the applicant:

1.   Exhibits knowledge of the elements related to airport/seaplane base, runway, and taxiway operations with emphasis on runway incursion avoidance. 1.17, 3.15, 7.5
2.   Properly identifies and interprets airport/seaplane base, runway and taxiway signs, markings, and lighting.....................1.17, 3.15, 7.5

IV.   AREA OF OPERATION: TAKEOFFS, LANDINGS, AND GO-AROUNDS

A.   Task: Normal And Crosswind Takeoff And Climb (ASEL and ASES)

NOTE: If a crosswind condition does not exist, the applicant's knowledge of crosswind elements shall be evaluated through oral testing.

DVD
Volume.Segment

Objective: To determine that the applicant:

1. Exhibits knowledge of the elements related to a normal and crosswind takeoff, climb operations, and rejected takeoff procedures. 1.19, 2.13, 7.10
2. Positions the flight controls for the existing wind conditions. 1.18, 2.13, 7.10
3. Clears the area; taxies into the takeoff position and aligns the airplane on the runway center/takeoff path. 1.19, 1.21
4. Retracts the water rudders, as appropriate, (ASES) and advances the throttle smoothly to takeoff power. 1.19, 7.10
5. Establishes and maintains the most efficient planing/lift-off attitude and corrects for porpoising and skipping (ASES). .... ASES Only
6. Lifts off at the recommended airspeed and accelerates to V_Y. 1.19, 7.10
7. Establishes a pitch attitude that will maintain V_Y, +10/-5 knots. 1.19, 1.21, 7.10
8. Retracts the landing gear, if appropriate, and flaps after a positive rate of climb is established. 7.10
9. Maintains takeoff power and V_Y, +10/-5 knots to a safe maneuvering altitude. 1.19, 7.10
10. Maintains directional control and proper wind-drift correction throughout the takeoff and climb. 1.19, 1.21, 2.13, 7.10
11. Complies with noise abatement procedures. ....7.12, Appendix E
12. Completes the appropriate checklist. ....7.10, AFM/POH

B.   Task: Normal And Crosswind Approach And Landing (ASEL and ASES)

Objective: To determine that the applicant:

1. Exhibits knowledge of the elements related to a normal and crosswind approach and landing. 2.11, 2.13, 7.10
2. Adequately surveys the intended landing area (ASES). ....ASES Only
3. Considers the wind conditions, landing surface, obstructions, and selects a suitable touchdown point. 1.18, 2.11
4. Establishes the recommended approach and landing configuration and airspeed, and adjusts pitch attitude and power as required. 2.11, 2.13
5. Maintains a stabilized approach and recommended airspeed, or in its absence, not more than 1.3 V_{SO}, +10/-5 knots, with wind gust factor applied. 2.11, 2.13, 7.10
6. Makes smooth, timely, and correct control application during the roundout and touchdown. 2.11, 2.13
7. Contacts the water at the proper pitch attitude (ASES). ....ASES Only
8. Touches down smoothly at the approximate stalling speed (ASEL). 2.11
9. Touches down at or within 400 feet (120 meters) beyond a specified point, with no drift, and with the airplane's longitudinal axis aligned with and over the runway center/landing path. 2.11, 2.13, 7.10
10. Maintains crosswind correction and directional control throughout the approach and landing sequence. 2.11, 2.13, 7.10
11. Completes the appropriate checklist. ....2.11, AFM/POH

C.   Task: Soft-Field Takeoff And Climb (ASEL)

Objective: To determine that the applicant:

1. Exhibits knowledge of the elements related to a soft-field takeoff and climb. 6.7, 7.10
2. Positions the flight controls for the existing wind conditions and to maximize lift as quickly as possible. 1.18, 2.13, 6.7
3. Clears the area; taxies onto the takeoff surface at a speed consistent with safety without stopping while advancing the throttle smoothly to takeoff power 6.7, 7.10
4. Establishes and maintains a pitch attitude that will transfer the weight of the airplane from the wheels to the wings as rapidly as possible. 6.7, 7.10
5. Lifts off at the lowest possible airspeed and remains in ground effect while accelerating to V_X or V_Y, as appropriate. 6.7, 7.10
6. Establishes the pitch attitude for V_X or V_Y, as appropriate, and maintains selected airspeed +10/-5 knots, during the climb. 6.7
7. Retracts the landing gear, if appropriate, and flaps after clear of any obstacles or as recommended by the manufacturer. 6.7
8. Maintains takeoff power and V_X or V_Y +10/-5 knots to a safe maneuvering altitude. 1.19, 7.10
9. Maintains directional control and proper wind-drift correction throughout the takeoff and climb. 1.19, 1.21, 2.13
10. Completes the appropriate checklist. ....7.10, AFM/POH

DVD
Volume.Segment

D. TASK: SOFT-FIELD APPROACH AND LANDING (ASEL)

Objective: To determine that the applicant:

1. Exhibits knowledge of the elements related to a soft-field approach and landing. 6.7, 7.10
2. Considers the wind conditions, landing surface and obstructions, and selects the most suitable touchdown point area...............1.18, 2.11
3. Establishes the recommended approach and landing configuration, and airspeed; adjusts pitch attitude and power as required...............6.7
4. Maintains a stabilized approach and recommended airspeed, or in its absence not more than 1.3 V_{SO}, +10/-5 knots, with wind gust factor applied. 6.7
5. Makes smooth, timely, and correct control application during the roundout and touchdown...............6.7
6. Touches down softly with no drift, and with the airplane's longitudinal axis aligned with the runway/landing path...............6.7
7. Maintains crosswind correction and directional control throughout the approach and landing...............2.11, 2.13
8. Maintains proper position of the flight controls and sufficient speed to taxi on the soft surface...............6.7
9. Completes the appropriate checklist. ....2.11, AFM/POH

E. TASK: SHORT-FIELD TAKEOFF (CONFINED AREA-ASES) AND MAXIMUM PERFORMANCE CLIMB (ASEL AND ASES)

Objective: To determine that the applicant:

1. Exhibits knowledge of the elements related to a short-field (confined area ASES) takeoff and maximum performance climb...............6.7, 7.10
2. Positions the flight controls for the existing wind conditions; sets the flaps as recommended...............1.18, 2.13, 6.7
3. Clears the area; taxies into takeoff position utilizing maximum available takeoff area and aligns the airplane on the runway center/takeoff path...............6.7
4. Selects an appropriate take off path for the existing conditions (ASES)...............ASES Only
5. Applies brakes (if appropriate), while advancing the throttle smoothly to takeoff power. 6.7
6. Establishes and maintains the most efficient planing/lift-off attitude and corrects for porpoising and skipping (ASES). .....ASES Only
7. Lifts off at the recommended airspeed, and accelerates to the recommended obstacle clearance airspeed or V_X...............6.7, 7.10
8. Establishes a pitch attitude that will maintain the recommended obstacle clearance airspeed, or V_X, +10/-5 knots, until the obstacle is cleared, or until the airplane is 50 feet (20 meters) above the surface...............6.7, 7.10
9. After clearing the obstacle, establishes the pitch attitude for V_Y, accelerates to V_Y, and maintains V_Y, +10/-5 knots, during the climb...............6.7, 7.10
10. Retracts the landing gear, if appropriate, and flaps after clear of any obstacles or as recommended by manufacturer...............6.7
11. Maintains takeoff power and V_Y, +10/-5 to a safe maneuvering altitude...............1.19, 7.10
12. Maintains directional control and proper wind-drift correction throughout the takeoff and climb...............1.19, 1.21, 2.13
13. Completes the appropriate checklist. ....7.10, AFM/POH

F. TASK: SHORT-FIELD APPROACH (CONFINED AREA-ASES) AND LANDING (ASEL AND ASES)

Objective: To determine that the applicant:

1. Exhibits knowledge of the elements related to a short-field (confined area ASES) approach and landing. 6.7, 7.10
2. Adequately surveys the intended landing area (ASES)...............ASES Only
3. Considers the wind conditions, landing surface, obstructions, and selects the most suitable touchdown point...............1.18, 2.11
4. Establishes the recommended approach and landing configuration and airspeed; adjusts pitch attitude and power as required. 6.7
5. Maintains a stabilized approach and the recommended approach airspeed, or in its absence not more than 1.3 V_{SO}, +10/-5 knots, with wind gust factor applied. 6.7
6. Makes smooth, timely, and correct control application during the roundout and touchdown...............6.7
7. Selects the proper landing path, contacts the water at the minimum safe airspeed with the proper pitch attitude for the surface conditions (ASES). ....ASES Only
8. Touches down smoothly at minimum control airspeed (ASEL). 6.7
9. Touches down at or within 200 feet (60 meters) beyond a specified point, with no side drift, minimum float and with the airplane's longitudinal axis aligned with and over the runway center/landing path...............7.10
10. Maintains crosswind correction and directional control throughout the approach and landing sequence. 2.11, 2.13
11. Applies brakes, (ASEL) or elevator control (ASES), as necessary, to stop in the shortest distance consistent with safety...............6.7
12. Completes the appropriate checklist. ....2.11, AFM/POH

G. **Task: Glassy Water Takeoff And Climb (ASES)**

NOTE: If a glassy water condition does not exist, the applicant shall be evaluated by simulating the TASK.

DVD
Volume.Segment

Objective: To determine that the applicant:

1. Exhibits knowledge of the elements related to glassy water takeoff and climb. .... ASES Only
2. Positions the flight controls and flaps for the existing conditions. .... ASES Only
3. Clears the area; selects an appropriate takeoff path considering surface hazards and/or vessels and surface conditions. .... ASES Only
4. Retracts the water rudders as appropriate; advances the throttle smoothly to takeoff power. .... ASES Only
5. Establishes and maintains an appropriate planing attitude, directional control, and corrects for porpoising, skipping, and increases in water drag. .... ASES Only
6. Utilizes appropriate techniques to lift seaplane from the water considering surface conditions. .... ASES Only
7. Establishes proper attitude/airspeed, and accelerates to V_Y, +10/-5 knots during the climb. .... ASES Only
8. Retracts the landing gear, if appropriate, and flaps after a positive rate of climb is established. .... ASES Only
9. Maintains takeoff power V_Y +10/-5 to a safe maneuvering altitude. .... ASES Only
10. Maintains directional control and proper wind-drift correction throughout takeoff and climb. .... ASES Only
11. Completes the appropriate checklist. .... ASES Only

H. **Task: Glassy Water Approach And Landing (ASES)**

NOTE: If a glassy water condition does not exist, the applicant shall be evaluated by simulating the TASK.

Objective: To determine that the applicant:

1. Exhibits knowledge of the elements related to glassy water approach and landing. .... ASES Only
2. Adequately surveys the intended landing area. .... ASES Only
3. Considers the wind conditions, water depth, hazards, surrounding terrain, and other watercraft. .... ASES Only
4. Selects the most suitable approach path, and touchdown area. .... ASES Only
5. Establishes the recommended approach and landing configuration and airspeed, and adjusts pitch attitude and power as required. .... ASES Only
6. Maintains a stabilized approach and the recommended approach airspeed, +10/-5 knots and maintains a touchdown pitch attitude and descent rate from the last altitude reference until touchdown. .... ASES Only
7. Makes smooth, timely, and correct power and control adjustments to maintain proper pitch attitude and rate of descent to touchdown. .... ASES Only
8. Contacts the water in the proper pitch attitude, and slows to idle taxi speed. .... ASES Only
9. Maintains crosswind correction and directional control throughout the approach and landing sequence .... ASES Only
10. Completes the appropriate checklist. .... ASES Only

I. **Task: Rough Water Takeoff And Climb (ASES)**

NOTE: If a rough water condition does not exist, the applicant shall be evaluated by simulating the TASK.

Objective: To determine that the applicant:

1. Exhibits knowledge of the elements related to rough water takeoff and climb. .... ASES Only
2. Positions the flight controls and flaps for the existing conditions. .... ASES Only
3. Clears the area; selects an appropriate takeoff path considering wind, swells surface hazards and/or vessels. .... ASES Only
4. Retracts the water rudders as appropriate; advances the throttle smoothly to takeoff power. .... ASES Only
5. Establishes and maintains an appropriate planing attitude, directional control, and corrects for porpoising, skipping, or excessive bouncing. .... ASES Only
6. Lifts off at minimum airspeed and accelerates to V_Y, +10/-5 knots before leaving ground effect. .... ASES Only
7. Retracts the landing gear, if appropriate, and flaps after a positive rate of climb is established. .... ASES Only
8. Maintains takeoff power V_Y +10/-5 to a safe maneuvering altitude. .... ASES Only
9. Maintains directional control and proper wind-drift correction throughout takeoff and climb. .... ASES Only
10. Completes the appropriate checklist. .... ASES Only

J. **Task: Rough Water Approach And Landing (ASES)**

NOTE: If a rough water condition does not exist, the applicant shall be evaluated by simulating the TASK.

Objective: To determine that the applicant:

1. Exhibits knowledge of the elements related to rough water approach and landing. .... ASES Only
2. Adequately surveys the intended landing area. .... ASES Only
3. Considers the wind conditions, water, depth, hazards, surrounding terrain, and other watercraft. .... ASES Only
4. Selects the most suitable approach path, and touchdown area. .... ASES Only
5. Establishes the recommended approach and landing configuration and airspeed, and adjusts pitch attitude and power as required. .... ASES Only
6. Maintains a stabilized approach and the recommended approach airspeed, or in its absence not more than 1.3 V_{SO} +10/-5 knots with wind gust factor applied. .... ASES Only
7. Makes smooth, timely, and correct power and control application during the roundout and touch down. .... ASES Only
8. Contacts the water in the proper pitch attitude, and at the proper airspeed, considering the type of rough water. .... ASES Only
9. Maintains crosswind correction and directional control throughout the approach and landing sequence. .... ASES Only
10. Completes the appropriate checklist. .... ASES Only

K. TASK: FORWARD SLIP TO A LANDING (ASEL AND ASES)
Objective: To determine that the applicant:

DVD
Volume.Segment

1. Exhibits knowledge of the elements related to a forward slip to a landing. 2.13, 7.10
2. Considers the wind conditions, landing surface and obstructions, and selects the most suitable touchdown point....................1.18, 2.11
3. Establishes the slipping attitude at the point from which a landing can be made using the
    recommended approach and landing configuration and airspeed; adjusts pitch attitude and
    power as required. 2.13
4. Maintains a ground track aligned with the runway center/landing path and an airspeed which results
    in minimum float during the roundout. 2.13
5. Makes smooth, timely, and correct control application during the recovery from the slip, the
    roundout, and the touchdown...2.13
6. Touches down smoothly at the approximate stalling speed, at or within 400 feet (120 meters) beyond
    a specified point, with no side drift, and with the airplane's longitudinal axis aligned with and over
    the runway center/landing path. 2.13
7. Maintains crosswind correction and directional control throughout the approach and landing sequence. 2.11, 2.13
8. Completes the appropriate checklist. ....2.11, AFM/POH

L. TASK: GO-AROUND/REJECTED LANDING (ASEL AND ASES)
Objective: To determine that the applicant:

1. Exhibits knowledge of the elements related to a go-around/rejected landing. 2.13, 7.10
2. Makes a timely decision to discontinue the approach to landing. 2.13
3. Applies takeoff power immediately and transitions to climb pitch attitude for V_y and maintains V_y +10/-5 knots. 2.13
4. Retracts the flaps as appropriate. 2.13
5. Retracts the landing gear, if appropriate, after a positive rate of climb is established.
6. Maneuvers to the side of the runway/landing area to clear and avoid conflicting traffic.
7. Maintains takeoff power V_y +10/-5 to a safe maneuvering altitude. 1.19, 7.10
8. Maintains directional control and proper wind-drift correction throughout the climb...............1.19, 1.21, 2.13
9. Completes the appropriate checklist. ....2.11, AFM/POH

V. AREA OF OPERATION: PERFORMANCE MANEUVER

DVD

A. TASK: STEEP TURNS (ASEL AND ASES)

Volume.Segment

Objective: To determine that the applicant:

1. Exhibits knowledge of the elements related to steep turns. 3.3, 7.10
2. Establishes the manufacturer's recommended airspeed or if one is not stated, a safe airspeed not to exceed V_A. 3.3, 7.10
3. Rolls into a coordinated 360° turn; maintains a 45° bank. 3.3, 7.10
4. Performs the task in the opposite direction, as specified by the examiner.
5. Divides attention between airplane control and orientation. 3.3
6. Maintains the entry altitude, ±100 feet (30 meters), airspeed, ±10 knots, bank, ±5°; and rolls out on
   the entry heading, ±10°. 3.3, 7.10

VI. AREA OF OPERATION: GROUND REFERENCE MANEUVERS

NOTE: The examiner shall select at least one TASK.

DVD
Volume.Segment

A. TASK: RECTANGULAR COURSE (ASEL AND ASES)

Objective: To determine that the applicant:

1. Exhibits knowledge of the elements related to a rectangular course. 1.18, 2.1, 7.10
2. Selects a suitable reference area. 2.1
3. Plans the maneuver so as to enter a left or right pattern, 600 to 1,000 feet AGL (180 to 300 meters) at an appropriate distance from the selected reference area, 45° to the downwind leg. 2.1
4. Applies adequate wind-drift correction during straight-and-turning flight to maintain a constant ground track around the rectangular reference area. 2.1
5. Divides attention between airplane control and the ground track while maintaining coordinated flight. 2.1, 7.10
6. Maintains altitude, ±100 feet (30 meters); maintains airspeed, ±10 knots.

B. TASK: S-TURNS (ASEL AND ASES)

Objective: To determine that the applicant:

1. Exhibits knowledge of the elements related to S-turns. 1.18, 3.1, 7.10
2. Selects a suitable ground reference line. 2.1
3. Plans the maneuver so as to enter at 600 to 1,000 feet (180 to 300 meters) AGL, perpendicular to the selected reference line. 2.1, 3.1
4. Applies adequate wind-drift correction to track a constant radius turn on each side of the selected reference line. 3.1
5. Reverses the direction of turn directly over the selected reference line. 3.1
6. Divides attention between airplane control and the ground track while maintaining coordinated flight. 2.1, 7.10
7. Maintains altitude, ±100 feet (30 meters); maintains airspeed, ±10 knots. 3.1

C. TASK: TURNS AROUND A POINT (ASEL AND ASES)

Objective: To determine that the applicant:

1. Exhibits knowledge of the elements related to turns around a point. 1.18, 3.1, 7.10
2. Selects a suitable ground reference point. 2.1
3. Plans the maneuver so as to enter left or right at 600 to 1,000 feet (180 to 300 meters) AGL, at an appropriate distance from the reference point. 2.1, 3.1
4. Applies adequate wind-drift correction to track a constant radius turn around the selected reference point. 3.1
5. Divides attention between airplane control and the ground track while maintaining coordinated flight. 2.1, 7.10
6. Maintains altitude, ±100 feet (30 meters); maintains airspeed, ±10 knots. 3.1

VII.   AREA OF OPERATION: NAVIGATION

A.   TASK: PILOTAGE AND DEAD RECKONING (ASEL AND ASES)

Objective: To determine that the applicant:

1. Exhibits knowledge of the elements related to pilotage and dead reckoning. 5.5, 5.15, 7.10
2. Follows the preplanned course by reference to landmarks. 5.15, 7.10
3. Identifies landmarks by relating surface features to chart symbols. 5.3, 5.15, 7.10
4. Navigates by means of precomputed headings, groundspeeds, and elapsed time. 5.15, 7.10
5. Corrects for and records the differences between preflight groundspeed and heading calculations and those determined en route. 5.15, 7.10
6. Verifies the airplane's position within three (3) nautical miles of the flight-planned route. 5.15, 7.10
7. Arrives at the en route checkpoints within five (5) minutes of the initial or revised ETA and provides a destination estimate. 7.10
8. Maintains the appropriate altitude, ±200 feet (60 meters) and headings, ±15°. 7.10

B.   TASK: NAVIGATION SYSTEMS AND RADAR SERVICES (ASEL AND ASES)

Objective: To determine that the applicant:

1. Exhibits knowledge of the elements related to navigation systems and radar services. 5.5, 5.7, 5.8, 5.9, 5.15, 6.1, 7.10
2. Demonstrates the ability to use an airborne electronic navigation system. 5.7, 5.8, 5.9, 5.15
3. Locates the airplane's position using the navigation system. 5.7, 5.8, 5.15, 7.10
4. Intercepts and tracks a given course, radial, or bearing, as appropriate. 5.7, 5.8, 5.9, 5.15, 7.10
5. Recognizes and describes the indication of station passage, if appropriate. 5.7, 7.10
6. Recognizes signal loss and takes appropriate action. 5.7, 7.10
7. Uses proper communication procedures when utilizing ATC radar services. 6.1, 6.18
8. Maintains the appropriate altitude, ±200 feet (60 meters) and headings ±15°.

C.   TASK: DIVERSION (ASEL AND ASES)

Objective: To determine that the applicant:

1. Exhibits knowledge of the elements related to diversion. 5.6, 6.18, 7.10
2. Selects an appropriate alternate airport and route. 5.6, 7.10
3. Makes an accurate estimate of heading, groundspeed, arrival time, and fuel consumption to the alternate airport. 7.10
4. Maintains the appropriate altitude, ±200 feet (60 meters) and heading, ±15°.

D.   TASK: LOST PROCEDURES (ASEL AND ASES)

Objective: To determine that the applicant:

1. Exhibits knowledge of the elements related to lost procedures. 6.18, 7.10
2. Selects an appropriate course of action. 6.18
3. Maintains an appropriate heading and climbs, if necessary. 6.18
4. Identifies prominent landmarks. 6.18, 7.10
5. Uses navigation systems/facilities and/or contacts an ATC facility for assistance, as appropriate. 6.18, 7.10

VIII. AREA OF OPERATION: SLOW FLIGHT AND STALLS

A. TASK: MANEUVERING DURING SLOW FLIGHT (ASEL AND ASES)   **DVD**
Objective: To determine that the applicant: **Volume.Segment**

1. Exhibits knowledge of the elements related to maneuvering during slow flight................................1.24, 6.13, 7.10
2. Selects an entry altitude that will allow the task to be completed no lower than 1,500 feet (460 meters) AGL...................................6.13
3. Establishes and maintains an airspeed at which any further increase in angle of attack, increase in load factor, or reduction in power, would result in an immediate stall.
4. Accomplishes coordinated straight-and-level flight, turns, climbs, and descents with landing gear and flap configurations specified by the examiner. 1.24
5. Divides attention between airplane control and orientation.
6. Maintains the specified altitude, ±100 feet (30 meters); specified heading, ±10°; airspeed, +10/–0 knots; and specified angle of bank, ±10°.

B. TASK: POWER-OFF STALLS (ASEL AND ASES)
Objective: To determine that the applicant:

1. Exhibits knowledge of the elements related to power-off stalls. 1.24, 2.9, 2.10, 7.10
2. Selects an entry altitude that allows the task to be completed no lower than 1,500 feet (460 meters) AGL. 2.9, 7.10
3. Establishes a stabilized descent in the approach or landing configuration, as specified by the examiner. 1.24, 2.9
4. Transitions smoothly from the approach or landing attitude to a pitch attitude that will induce a stall.......................................1.24, 2.9
5. Maintains a specified heading, ±10°, in straight flight; maintains a specified angle of bank not to exceed 20°, ±10°, in turning flight, while inducing the stall. 1.24
6. Recognizes and recovers promptly after the stall occurs by simultaneously reducing the angle of attack, increasing power to maximum allowable, and leveling the wings to return to a straight-and-level flight attitude with a minimum loss of altitude appropriate for the airplane....................................1.24, 2.9, 7.10
7. Retracts the flaps to the recommended setting; retracts the landing gear, if retractable, after a positive rate of climb is established...2.9
8. Accelerates to V_X or V_Y speed before the final flap retraction; returns to the altitude, heading, and airspeed specified by the examiner. 2.9

C. TASK: POWER-ON STALLS (ASEL AND ASES)
NOTE: In some high performance airplanes, the power setting may have to be reduced below the practical test standards guideline power setting to prevent excessively high pitch attitudes (greater than 30° nose up).

Objective: To determine that the applicant:

1. Exhibits knowledge of the elements related to power-on stalls...1.24, 2.9, 2.10, 7.10
2. Selects an entry altitude that allows the task to be completed no lower than 1,500 feet (460 meters) AGL. 2.9, 7.10
3. Establishes the takeoff or departure configuration. Sets power to no less than 65 percent available power. 2.9
4. Transitions smoothly from the takeoff or departure attitude to the pitch attitude that will induce a stall...........................2.9
5. Maintains a specified heading, ±10°, in straight flight; maintains a specified angle of bank not to exceed 20°, ±10°, in turning flight, while inducing the stall. 2.9, 7.10
6. Recognizes and recovers promptly after the stall occurs by simultaneously reducing the angle of attack, increasing power as appropriate, and leveling the wings to return to a straight-and-level flight attitude with a minimum loss of altitude appropriate for the airplane...2.9, 7.10
7. Retracts the flaps to the recommended setting; retracts the landing gear if retractable, after a positive rate of climb is established..2.9
8. Accelerates to V_X or V_Y speed before the final flap retraction; returns to the altitude, heading, and airspeed specified by the examiner. 2.9

D. TASK: SPIN AWARENESS (ASEL AND ASES)
Objective: To determine that the applicant exhibits knowledge of the elements related to spin awareness by explaining:

1. Aerodynamic factors related to spins...2.10
2. Flight situations where unintentional spins may occur..2.10
3. Procedures for recovery from unintentional spins...2.10

IX.   AREA OF OPERATION: BASIC INSTRUMENT MANEUVERS

NOTE: The examiner shall select task E and at least two other TASKs.

**DVD
Volume.Segment**

A.   TASK: STRAIGHT-AND-LEVEL FLIGHT (ASEL AND ASES)

Objective: To determine that the applicant:

1.   Exhibits knowledge of the elements related to attitude instrument flying during straight-and-level flight. 6.14, 7.10
2.   Maintains straight-and-level flight solely by reference to instruments using proper instrument
cross-check and interpretation, and coordinated control application..6.14
3.   Maintains altitude, ±200 feet (60 meters); heading, ±20°; and airspeed, ±10 knots. 7.10

B.   TASK: CONSTANT AIRSPEED CLIMBS (ASEL AND ASES)

Objective: To determine that the aₗ plicant:

1.   Exhibits knowledge of the elements related to attitude instrument flying during constant airspeed climbs..........................6.14, 7.10
2.   Establishes the climb configuration specified by the examiner..6.14
3.   Transitions to the climb pitch attitude and power setting on an assigned heading using proper
instrument cross-check and interpretation, and coordinated control application. 6.14
4.   Demonstrates climbs solely by reference to instruments at a constant airspeed to specific altitudes in
straight flight and turns. 6.14
5.   Levels off at the assigned altitude and maintains that altitude, ±200 feet (60 meters); maintains
heading, ±20°; maintains airspeed, ±10 knots. 7.10

C.   TASK: CONSTANT AIRSPEED DESCENTS (ASEL AND ASES)

Objective: To determine that the applicant:

1.   Exhibits knowledge of the elements related to attitude instrument flying during constant airspeed descents..........................6.14, 7.10
2.   Establishes the descent configuration specified by the examiner...6.14
3.   Transitions to the descent pitch attitude and power setting on an assigned heading using proper
instrument cross-check and interpretation, and coordinated control application. 6.14
4.   Demonstrates descents solely by reference to instruments at a constant airspeed to specific altitudes
in straight flight and turns..6.14
5.   Levels off at the assigned altitude and maintains that altitude, ±200 feet (60 meters); maintains
heading, ±20°; maintains airspeed, ±10 knots. 7.10

D.   TASK: TURNS TO HEADINGS (ASEL AND ASES)

Objective: To determine that the applicant:

1.   Exhibits knowledge of the elements related to attitude instrument flying during turns to headings....................6.14, 7.10
2.   Transitions to the level-turn attitude using proper instrument cross-check and interpretation, and
coordinated control application...6.14
3.   Demonstrates turns to headings solely by reference to instruments; maintains altitude, ±200 feet
(60 meters); maintains a standard rate turn and rolls out on the assigned heading, ±10°; maintains
airspeed, ±10 knots.

E.   TASK: RECOVERY FROM UNUSUAL FLIGHT ATTITUDES (ASEL AND ASES)

Objective: To determine that the applicant:

1.   Exhibits knowledge of the elements related to attitude instrument flying during unusual attitudes. 6.14, 7.10
2.   Recognizes unusual flight attitudes solely by reference to instruments; recovers promptly to a
stabilized level flight attitude using proper instrument cross-check and interpretation and smooth,
coordinated control application in the correct sequence...6.14, 7.10

F.   TASK: RADIO COMMUNICATIONS, NAVIGATION SYSTEMS/FACILITIES, AND RADAR SERVICES (ASEL AND ASES)

Objective: To determine that the applicant:

1.   Exhibits knowledge of the elements related to radio communications, navigation systems/facilities,
and radar services available for use during flight solely by reference to instruments............................5.7, 5.8, 5.9, 6.14, 7.10
2.   Selects the proper frequency and identifies the appropriate facility..5.7
3.   Follows verbal instructions and/or navigation systems/facilities for guidance. 5.7, 5.8, 5.9, 7.10
4.   Determines the minimum safe altitude. ....Appendix F
5.   Maintains altitude, ±200 feet (60 meters); maintains heading, ±20°; maintains airspeed, ±10 knots.

X.   AREA OF OPERATION: EMERGENCY OPERATIONS

DVD
Volume.Segment

A.   TASK: EMERGENCY APPROACH AND LANDING (ASEL AND ASES)

Objective: To determine that the applicant:

1. Exhibits knowledge of the elements related to emergency approach and landing procedures..3.5, 7.10
2. Analyzes the situation and selects an appropriate course of action.
3. Establishes and maintains the recommended best-glide airspeed, ±10 knots..3.5, 7.10
4. Selects a suitable landing area. 3.5, 7.10
5. Plans and follows a flight pattern to the selected landing area considering altitude, wind, terrain, and obstructions...................3.5, 7.10
6. Prepares for landing, or go-around, as specified by the examiner.
7. Follows the appropriate checklist. ....3.5, 7.10, AFM/POH

B.   TASK: SYSTEMS AND EQUIPMENT MALFUNCTIONS (ASEL AND ASES)

Objective: To determine that the applicant:

1. Exhibits knowledge of the elements related to system and equipment malfunctions appropriate to the
airplane provided for the practical test...7.10
2. Analyzes the situation and takes appropriate action for simulated emergencies appropriate to the
airplane provided for the practical test for at least three (3) of the following-...7.10
    a) partial or complete power loss. 3.5, 7.10
    b) engine roughness or overheat..7.10
    c) carburetor or induction icing..1.11, 7.10
    d) loss of oil pressure. 7.10
    e) fuel starvation...7.10
    f) electrical malfunction..AFM/POH
    g) vacuum/pressure, and associated flight instruments malfunction..AFM/POH
    h) pitot/static...3.5
    i) landing gear or flap malfunction...AFM/POH
    j) inoperative trim..AFM/POH
    k) inadvertent door or window opening. ....AFM/POH
    l) structural icing. ....AFM/POH
    m) smoke/fire/engine compartment fire..AFM/POH
    n) any other emergency appropriate to the airplane provided for the flight test. ....AFM/POH
3. Follows the appropriate checklist or procedure. ....AFM/POH

C.   TASK: EMERGENCY EQUIPMENT AND SURVIVAL GEAR (ASEL AND ASES)

Objective: To determine that the applicant:

1. Exhibits knowledge of the elements related to emergency equipment and survival gear appropriate to
the airplane and environment encountered during flight. Identifies appropriate equipment that should
be aboard the airplane. .... AFM/POH, Appendix G

XI.   AREA OF OPERATION: NIGHT OPERATIONS

A.   TASK: NIGHT PREPARATION (ASEL AND ASES)   **DVD**
Objective: To determine that the applicant exhibits knowledge of the elements related to night operations by   **Volume.Segment**
explaining:

1.   Physiological aspects of night flying as it relates to vision. 5.1, 7.10
2.   Lighting systems identifying airports, runways, taxiways and obstructions, and pilot controlled lighting. 5.1, 7.10
3.   Airplane lighting systems. 5.1, 7.10
4.   Personal equipment essential for night flight...5.1, 7.10
5.   Night orientation, navigation, and chart reading techniques. 5.2
6.   Safety precautions and emergencies unique to night flying. 7.10

XII. AREA OF OPERATION: POSTFLIGHT PROCEDURES

DVD
Volume.Segment

A. TASK: AFTER LANDING, PARKING, AND SECURING (ASEL AND ASES)

Objective: To determine that the applicant:

1. Exhibits knowledge of the elements related to after landing, parking and securing procedures. 2.11, 7.10
2. Maintains directional control after touchdown while decelerating to an appropriate speed.
3. Observes runway hold lines and other surface control markings and lighting. 3.15
4. Parks in an appropriate area, considering the safety of nearby persons and property. 7.10
5. Follows the appropriate procedure for engine shutdown. 2.11
6. Completes the appropriate checklist. .... 2.11, 7.10, AFM/POH
7. Conducts an appropriate postflight inspection and secures the aircraft. .... AFM/POH

B. TASK: ANCHORING (ASES)

Objective: To determine that the applicant:

1. Exhibits knowledge of the elements related to anchoring. .... ASES Only
2. Selects a suitable area for anchoring, considering seaplane movement, water depth, tide, wind, and weather changes. .... ASES Only
3. Uses an adequate number of anchors and lines of sufficient strength and length to ensure the seaplane's security .... ASES Only

C. TASK: DOCKING AND MOORING (ASES)

Objective: To determine that the applicant:

1. Exhibits knowledge of the elements related to docking and mooring. .... ASES Only
2. Approaches the dock or mooring buoy in the proper direction considering speed, hazards, wind, and water current. .... ASES Only
3. Ensures seaplane security. .... ASES Only

D. TASK: RAMPING/BEACHING (ASES)

Objective: To determine that the applicant:

1. Exhibits knowledge of the elements related to ramping/beaching. .... ASES Only
2. Approaches the ramp/beach considering persons and property, in the proper attitude and direction, at
   a safe speed, considering water depth, tide, current and wind. .... ASES Only
3. Ramps/beaches and secures the seaplane in a manner that will protect it from the harmful effect of
   wind, waves, and changes in water level. .... ASES Only

Supplemental PTS Information

The following information is from the Private Pilot Practical Test Standards and may be useful in your preparation.

Practical Test Standards Description

Areas of Operation are phases of the practical test arranged in a logical sequence within each standard. They begin with Preflight Preparation, and end with Postflight Procedures. The examiner, however, may conduct the practical test in any sequence that will result in a complete and efficient test; **however, the ground portion of the practical test shall be accomplished before the flight portion.**

Tasks are titles of knowledge areas, flight procedures, or maneuvers appropriate to an Area of Operation. The abbreviation(s) within parentheses immediately following a Task refer to the category and/or class aircraft appropriate to that Task. The meaning of each abbreviation is as follows.

> **ASEL**   Airplane—Single-Engine Land
>
> **ASES**   Airplane—Single-Engine Sea

NOTE: When administering a test based on this PTS, the Tasks appropriate to the class airplane (ASEL or ASES) used for the test shall be included in the plan of action. The absence of a class indicates the Task is for all classes.

Note is used to emphasize special considerations required in the Area of Operation or Task.

The **Objective** lists the elements that must be satisfactorily performed to demonstrate competency in a Task. The Objective includes:

1) specifically what the applicant should be able to do;

2) the conditions under which the Task is to be performed; and

3) the minimum acceptable standards of performance.

Use of the Practical Test Standards Book

The FAA requires that that all private pilot practical tests be conducted in accordance with the appropriate Private Pilot Practical Test Standard and the policies set forth in this Introduction. Applicants shall be evaluated in **ALL** Tasks included in each Area of Operation of the appropriate practical test standard, unless otherwise noted.

An applicant, who holds at least a private pilot certificate seeking an additional airplane category rating and/or class rating at the private pilot level, shall be evaluated in the Areas of Operation and Tasks listed in the Additional Rating Task Table. At the discretion of the examiner, an evaluation of the applicant's competence in the remaining Areas of Operation and Tasks may be conducted.

If the applicant holds two or more category or class ratings at least at the private level, and the ratings table indicates differing required Tasks, the "least restrictive" entry applies. For example, if "ALL" and "NONE" are indicated for one Area of Operation, the "NONE" entry applies. If "B" and "B, C" are indicated, the "B" entry applies.

In preparation for the practical test, the examiner shall develop a written "plan of action." The "plan of action" shall include all Tasks in each Area of Operation, unless noted otherwise. If the elements in one Task have already been evaluated in another Task, they need not be repeated. For example, the "plan of action" need not include evaluating the applicant on complying with markings, signals, and clearances at the end of the flight, if that element was sufficiently observed at the beginning of the flight. **Any Task selected for evaluation during a practical test shall be evaluated in its entirety.**

The examiner is not required to follow the precise order in which the Areas of Operation and Tasks appear in this book. The examiner may change the sequence or combine Tasks with similar Objectives to have an orderly and efficient flow of the practical test. For example, Radio Communications and ATC Light Signals may be combined with Traffic Patterns. The examiner's "plan of action" shall include the order and combination of Tasks to be demonstrated by the applicant in a manner that will result in an efficient and valid test.

The examiner is expected to use good judgment in the performance of simulated emergency procedures. The use of the safest means for simulation is expected. Consideration must be given to local conditions, both meteorological and topographical, at the time of the test, as well as the applicant's workload, and the condition of the aircraft used. If the procedure being evaluated would jeopardize safety, it is expected that the applicant will simulate that portion of the maneuver.

Special Emphasis Areas

Examiners shall place special emphasis upon areas of aircraft operations considered critical to flight safety. Among these are:

1) positive aircraft control;

2) procedures for positive exchange of flight controls (who is flying the airplane);

3) stall/spin awareness;

4) collision avoidance;

5) wake turbulence avoidance;

6) Land and Hold Short Operations (LAHSO);

7) runway incursion avoidance;

8) controlled flight into terrain (CFIT);

9) aeronautical decision making (ADM);

10) checklist usage; and

11) other areas deemed appropriate to any phase of the practical test.

Although these areas may not be specifically addressed under each **Task, they are essential to flight safety and will be evaluated during** the practical test. In all instances, the applicant's actions will relate to the complete situation.

Private Pilot - Airplane Practical Test Prerequisites

An applicant for the Private Pilot—Airplane Practical Test is required by 14 CFR part 61 to:

1) be at least 17 years of age;

2) be able to read, speak, write, and understand the English language. If there is a doubt, use AC 60-28, English Language Skill Standards;

3) have passed the appropriate private pilot knowledge test since the beginning of the 24th month before the month in which he or she takes the practical test;

4) have satisfactorily accomplished the required training and obtained the aeronautical experience prescribed;

5) possess at least a current third class medical certificate;

6) have an endorsement from an authorized instructor certifying that the applicant has received and logged training time within 60 days preceding the date of application in preparation for the practical test, and is prepared for the practical test; and

7) also have an endorsement certifying that the applicant has demonstrated satisfactory knowledge of the subject areas in which the applicant was deficient on the airman knowledge test.

Aircraft and Equipment Required for the Practical Test

The private pilot—airplane applicant is required by 14 CFR section 61.45, to provide an airworthy, certificated aircraft for use during the practical test. This section further requires that the aircraft must:

1) be of U.S., foreign or military registry of the same category, class, and type, if applicable, for the certificate and/or rating for which the applicant is applying;

2) have fully functioning dual controls, except as provided for in 14 CFR section 61.45(c) and (e); and

3) be capable of performing all Areas of Operation appropriate to the rating sought and have no operating limitations, which prohibit its use in any of the Areas of Operation, required for the practical test.

Flight Instructor Responsibility

An appropriately rated flight instructor is responsible for training the private pilot applicant to acceptable standards in all subject matter areas, procedures, and maneuvers included in the Tasks within each Area of Operation in the appropriate private pilot practical test standard.

Because of the impact of their teaching activities in developing safe, proficient pilots, flight instructors should exhibit a high level of knowledge, skill, and the ability to impart that knowledge and skill to students.

Throughout the applicant's training, the flight instructor is responsible for emphasizing the performance of effective visual scanning and collision avoidance procedures.

Examiner Responsibility

The examiner conducting the practical test is responsible for determining that the applicant meets the acceptable standards of knowledge and skill of each Task within the appropriate practical test standard. Since there is no formal division between the "oral" and "skill" portions of the practical test, this becomes an ongoing process throughout the test. Oral questioning, to determine the applicant's knowledge of Tasks and related safety factors, should be used judiciously at all times, especially during the flight portion of the practical test. Examiners shall test to the greatest extent practicable the applicant's correlative abilities rather than mere rote enumeration of facts throughout the practical test.

If the examiner determines that a Task is incomplete, or the outcome uncertain, the examiner may require the applicant to repeat that Task, or portions of that Task. This provision has been made in the interest of fairness and does not mean that instruction, practice, or the repeating of an unsatisfactory task is permitted during the certification process. When practical, the remaining Tasks of the practical test phase should be completed before repeating the questionable Task.

Throughout the flight portion of the practical test, the examiner shall evaluate the applicant's use of visual scanning and collision avoidance procedures.

Note: The word "examiner" is used throughout the standards to denote either the FAA inspector or FAA designated pilot examiner who conducts an official practical test.

Satisfactory Performance

Satisfactory performance to meet the requirements for certification is based on the applicant's ability to safely:

1) perform the Tasks specified in the Areas of Operation for the certificate or rating sought within the approved standards;

2) demonstrate mastery of the aircraft with the successful outcome of each Task performed never seriously in doubt;

3) demonstrate satisfactory proficiency and competency within the approved standards;

4) demonstrate sound judgment; and

5) demonstrate single-pilot competence if the aircraft is type certificated for single-pilot operations.

Unsatisfactory Performance

The tolerances represent the performance expected in good flying conditions. If, in the judgment of the examiner, the applicant does not meet the standards of performance of any Task performed, the associated Area of Operation is failed and therefore, the practical test is failed.

The examiner or applicant may discontinue the test at any time when the failure of an Area of Operation makes the applicant ineligible for the certificate or rating sought. The test may be continued ONLY with the consent of the applicant. If the test is discontinued, the applicant is entitled credit for only those Areas of Operation and their associated Tasks satisfactorily performed. However, during the retest, and at the discretion of the examiner, any Task may be reevaluated, including those previously passed.

Typical areas of unsatisfactory performance and grounds for disqualification are:

1) Any action or lack of action by the applicant which requires corrective intervention by the examiner to maintain safe flight.

2) Failure to use proper and effective visual scanning techniques to clear the area before and while performing maneuvers.

3) Consistently exceeding tolerances stated in the Objectives.

4) Failure to take prompt corrective action when tolerances are exceeded.

When a notice of disapproval is issued, the examiner shall record the applicant's unsatisfactory performance in terms of the Area of Operation and specific Task(s) not meeting the standard appropriate to the practical test conducted. The Area(s) of Operation/Task(s) not tested and the number of practical test failures shall also be recorded. If the applicant fails the practical test because of a special emphasis area, the Notice of Disapproval shall indicate the associated Task. i.e.: Area of Operation VIII, Maneuvering During Slow Flight, failure to use proper collision avoidance procedures.

Crew Resource Management (CRM)

CRM refers to the effective use of all available resources: human resources, hardware, and information. Human resources include all groups routinely working with the cockpit crew or pilot who are involved with decisions that are required to operate a flight safely. These groups include, but are not limited to dispatchers, cabin crewmembers, maintenance personnel, air traffic controllers, and weather services. CRM is not a single Task, but a set of competencies that must be evident in all Tasks in this practical test standard as applied to either single pilot operations or crew.

Applicant's Use of Checklists

Throughout the practical test, the applicant is evaluated on the use of an appropriate checklist. Proper use is dependent on the specific Task being evaluated. The situation may be such that the use of the checklist, while accomplishing elements of an Objective, would be either unsafe or impractical, especially in a single-pilot operation. In this case, a review of the checklist after the elements have been accomplished, would be appropriate. Division of attention and proper visual scanning should be considered when using a checklist.

Use of Distractions During Practical Tests

Numerous studies indicate that many accidents have occurred when the pilot has been distracted during critical phases of flight. To evaluate the applicant's ability to utilize proper control technique while dividing attention both inside and/or outside the cockpit, the examiner shall cause realistic distractions during the flight portion of the practical test to evaluate the applicant's ability to divide attention while maintaining safe flight.

Positive Exchange of Flight Controls

During flight training, there must always be a clear understanding between students and flight instructors of who has control of the aircraft. Prior to flight, a briefing should be conducted that includes the procedure for the exchange of flight controls. A positive three-step process in the exchange of flight controls between pilots is a proven procedure and one that is strongly recommended.

When the instructor wishes the student to take control of the aircraft, he or she will say, "You have the flight controls." The student acknowledges immediately by saying, "I have the flight controls." The flight instructor again says, "You have the flight controls." When control is returned to the instructor, follow the same procedure. A visual check is recommended to verify that the exchange has occurred. There should never by any doubt as to who is flying the aircraft.

Metric Conversion Initiative

To assist pilots in understanding and using the metric measurement system, the practical test standards refer to the metric equivalent of various altitudes throughout. The inclusion of meters is intended to familiarize pilots with its use. The metric altimeter is arranged in 10 meter increments; therefore, when converting from feet to meters, the exact conversion, being too exact for practical purposes, is rounded to the nearest 10 meter increment or even altitude as necessary.

Additional Rating Task Table – Airplane Single-Engine Land

Addition of an Airplane Single-Engine Land Rating to an existing Private Pilot Certificate								
Required TASKs are indicated by either the TASK letter(s) that apply(s) or an indication that all or none of the TASKs must be tested based on the notes in each AREA OF OPERATION.								
PRIVATE PILOT RATING(S) HELD								
AREAS OF OPERATION	ASES	AMEL	AMES	RH	RG	Glider	Balloon	Airship
I	F,G	F,G	F,G	F,G	F,G	F,G	F,G	F,G
II	D	NONE	D	A,C,D, F	A,D,F	A,B,C, D,F	A,B,C, D,F	A,B,C, D,F
III	C	NONE	C	B,C	NONE	B,C	B,C	B,C
IV	A,B,C, D,E,F	A,B,C, D,E,F	A,B,C, D,E,F	A,B,C, D,E,F, K,L	A,B,C, D,E,F, K,L	A,B,C, D,E,F, K,L	A,B,C, D,E,F, K,L	A,B,C, D,E,F, K,L
V	NONE	NONE	NONE	ALL	ALL	ALL	ALL	ALL
VI	NONE	NONE	NONE	ALL	NONE	ALL	ALL	ALL
VII	NONE	NONE	NONE	NONE	NONE	ALL	ALL	NONE
VIII	NONE	NONE	NONE	ALL	ALL	ALL	ALL	ALL
IX	NONE	NONE	NONE	ALL	ALL	ALL	ALL	ALL
X	A,B	A,B	A,B	ALL	ALL	ALL	ALL	ALL
XI	NONE	NONE	NONE	NONE	NONE	ALL	ALL	ALL
XII	A	NONE	A	A	A	A	A	A

Applicant's Practical Test Checklist

APPOINTMENT WITH EXAMINER:

EXAMINER'S NAME_____

LOCATION _____

DATE/TIME _____

ACCEPTABLE AIRCRAFT
- ❑ Aircraft Documents:
    - Airworthiness Certificate
    - Registration Certificate
    - Operating Limitations
- ❑ Aircraft Maintenance Records:
    - Logbook Record of Airworthiness Inspections and AD Compliance
- ❑ Pilot's Operating Handbook, FAA-Approved Airplane Flight Manual

PERSONAL EQUIPMENT
- ❑ View-Limiting Device
- ❑ Current Aeronautical Charts
- ❑ Computer and Plotter
- ❑ Flight Plan Form
- ❑ Flight Logs
- ❑ Current AIM, Airport Facility Directory, and Appropriate Publications

PERSONAL RECORDS
- ❑ Identification - Photo/Signature ID
- ❑ Pilot Certificate
- ❑ Current and Appropriate Medical Certificate
- ❑ Completed FAA Form 8710-1, Airman Certificate and/or Rating Application with Instructor's Signature (if applicable)
- ❑ Computer Test Report
- ❑ Pilot Logbook with Appropriate Instructor Endorsements
- ❑ FAA Form 8060-5, Notice of Disapproval (if applicable)
- ❑ Approved School Graduation Certificate (if applicable)
- ❑ Examiner's Fee (if applicable)

Examiner's Practical Test Checklist

(ASEL & ASES)

APPLICANT'S NAME_____

LOCATION_____

DATE/TIME_____

I. PREFLIGHT PREPARATION
- ❑ A. Certificates and Documents (ASEL and ASES)
- ❑ B. Airworthiness Requirements (ASEL and ASES)
- ❑ C. Weather Information (ASEL and ASES)
- ❑ D. Cross-Country Flight Planning (ASEL and ASES)
- ❑ E. National Airspace System (ASEL and ASES)
- ❑ F. Performance and Limitations (ASEL and ASES)
- ❑ G. Operation of Systems (ASEL and ASES)
- ❑ H. Water and Seaplane Characteristics (ASES)
- ❑ I. Seaplane Bases, Maritime Rules, and Aids to Marine Navigation (ASES)
- ❑ J. Aeromedical Factors (ASEL and ASES)

II. PREFLIGHT PROCEDURES
- ❑ A. Preflight Inspection (ASEL and ASES)
- ❑ B. Cockpit Management (ASEL and ASES)
- ❑ C. Engine Starting (ASEL and ASES)
- ❑ D. Taxiing (ASEL)
- ❑ E. Taxiing and Sailing (ASES)
- ❑ F. Before Takeoff Check (ASEL and ASES)

III. AIRPORT AND SEAPLANE BASE OPERATIONS
- ❑ A. Radio Communications and ATC Light Signals (ASEL and ASES)
- ❑ B. Traffic Patterns (ASEL and ASES)
- ❑ C. Airport/Seaplane Base, Runway, and Taxiway Signs, Markings, and Lighting (ASEL and ASES)

IV. TAKEOFFS, LANDINGS, AND GO-AROUNDS
- ❑ A. Normal and Crosswind Takeoff and Climb (ASEL and ASES)
- ❑ B. Normal and Crosswind Approach and Landing (ASEL and ASES)
- ❑ C. Soft-Field Takeoff and Climb (ASEL)
- ❑ D. Soft-Field Approach and Landing (ASEL)
- ❑ E. Short-Field (Confined Area—ASES) Takeoff and Maximum Performance Climb (ASEL and ASES)
- ❑ F. Short-Field Approach (Confined Area—ASES) and Landing (ASEL and ASES)
- ❑ G. Glassy Water Takeoff and Climb (ASES)
- ❑ H. Glassy Water Approach and Landing (ASES)
- ❑ I. Rough Water Takeoff and Climb (ASES)
- ❑ J. Rough Water Approach and Landing (ASES)
- ❑ K. Forward Slip to a Landing (ASEL and ASES)
- ❑ L. Go-Around/Rejected Landing (ASEL and ASES)

V. PERFORMANCE MANEUVER
- ❑ A. Steep Turns (ASEL and ASES)

VI. GROUND REFERENCE MANEUVERS
- ❑ A. Rectangular Course (ASEL and ASES)
- ❑ B. S-Turns (ASEL and ASES)
- ❑ C. Turns Around a Point (ASEL and ASES)

VII. NAVIGATION
- ❑ A. Pilotage and Dead Reckoning (ASEL and ASES)
- ❑ B. Navigation Systems and Radar Services (ASEL and ASES)
- ❑ C. Diversion (ASEL and ASES)
- ❑ D. Lost Procedures (ASEL and ASES)

VIII. SLOW FLIGHT AND STALLS
- ❏ A. Maneuvering During Slow Flight (ASEL and ASES)
- ❏ B. Power-Off Stalls (ASEL and ASES)
- ❏ C. Power-On Stalls (ASEL and ASES)
- ❏ D. Spin Awareness (ASEL and ASES)

IX. BASIC INSTRUMENT MANEUVERS
- ❏ A. Straight-and-Level Flight (ASEL and ASES)
- ❏ B. Constant Airspeed Climbs (ASEL and ASES)
- ❏ C. Constant Airspeed Descents (ASEL and ASES)
- ❏ D. Turns to Headings (ASEL and ASES)
- ❏ E. Recovery from Unusual Flight Attitudes (ASEL and ASES)
- ❏ F. Radio Communications, Navigation Systems/Facilities, and Radar Services (ASEL and ASES)

X. EMERGENCY OPERATIONS
- ❏ A. Emergency Approach and Landing (Simulated) (ASEL and ASES)
- ❏ B. Systems and Equipment Malfunctions (ASEL and ASES)
- ❏ C. Emergency Equipment and Survival Gear (ASEL and ASES)

XI. NIGHT OPERATION
- ❏ A. Night Preparation (ASEL and ASES)

XII. POSTFLIGHT PROCEDURES
- ❏ A. After Landing, Parking, and Securing (ASEL and ASES)
- ❏ B. Anchoring (ASES)
- ❏ C. Docking and Mooring (ASES)
- ❏ D. Ramping/Beaching (ASES)

Page Intentionally Left Blank

Section 2 - Private Pilot DVD Study Guide

The following pages should be used as reinforcing material while reviewing the various DVD volumes.

Please remember these notes cannot serve as a substitute for the instruction contained in the video. They are intended to reinforce essential material from the *What You Should Know* DVD Series and will assist you in learning these subjects.

Volume 1 - Your First Few Hours

Aerodynamics

1) Taxiing

    a) The figure below shows crosswinds at "A," "B," "C," and "D:"

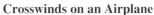

Crosswinds on an Airplane

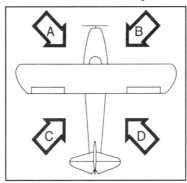

    b) The pictured crosswinds should be addressed with the control inputs noted below:

Pictured Crosswind	Aileron Positions	Tricycle Gear Elevator Position	Tricycle Gear Control Yoke or Stick Position	Conventional Gear Elevator Position	Conventional Gear Control Yoke or Stick Position
A--Left, quartering headwind	Left aileron up, right aileron down	Elevator neutral	Left and neutral	Elevator neutral or slightly up	Left and neutral or slightly back
B--Right, quartering headwind	Right aileron up, left aileron down	Elevator neutral	Right and neutral	Elevator neutral or slightly up	Right and neutral or slightly back
C--Left, quartering tailwind	Left aileron down, right aileron up	Elevator down	Right and forward	Elevator down	Right and forward
D--Right, quartering tailwind	Right aileron down, left aileron up	Elevator down	Left and forward	Elevator down	Left and forward

    c) Remember these guidelines:

        i) Turn the ailerons away from a quartering tailwind when taxiing.

        ii) Turn the ailerons into a quartering headwind when taxiing.

        iii) Quartering tailwinds are critical since they can cause high wing airplanes to flip over on their back.

        iv) Keep the elevator neutral in a headwind in a tricycle-gear airplane; elevator up in a headwind in a tailwheel airplane.

        v) Keep the elevator down in a tailwind in a tricycle-gear or a tailwheel airplane.

Engines/Preflight

1) If the recommended octane is not available for an aircraft, do not use a fuel that has a lower-than-specified fuel rating. Instead, use the next higher octane aviation gasoline.

2) After starting an aircraft engine, adjust to recommended warm-up settings and then check engine gauge indications.

3) It is extremely important that a competent pilot be at the controls in the cockpit when hand propping an airplane engine.

Federal Aviation Regulations

1) A pilot must have a photo identification in his physical possession or readily accessible in the aircraft when exercising the privileges of a pilot certificate.

2) The photo identification must be one of the following:
   a) Valid U.S. driver's license.
   b) U.S. issued federal or state identification card.
   c) U.S. Armed Forces' identification card.
   d) Official passport.
   e) Credential that authorizes unescorted access to a security identification display area at an airport regulated under 49 CFR part 1542.
   f) Other form of identification that the Administrator finds acceptable.

Volume 2 - Practicing Landings

Engines/Preflight

1) The basic purpose of adjusting the fuel/air mixture at altitude is to decrease the fuel flow in order to compensate for decreased air density.

   a) The fuel/air mixture may become excessively lean if a descent is made to a lower altitude without readjusting the mixture.

   b) If, during the run-up at a high-elevation airport, a pilot notes a slight engine roughness that is not affected by the magneto check but grows worse during the carb heat check, better results may be obtained with a leaner fuel mixture.

   c) Oil temperature gauges that have exceeded their normal operating range may indicate a fuel mixture set too lean, too much power, detonation, or a low oil level.

2) The operating principle of float-type carburetors is based on the difference in air pressure at the venturi throat and the air inlet.

3) If **detonation** occurs during climb-out, lower the nose slightly to increase airspeed and cooling.

4) A pilot can avoid engine overheating by increasing airspeed, enriching the mixture, or reducing power.

5) Excessively high engine temperatures will cause loss of power, excessive oil consumption, and possible permanent internal engine damage.

Aerodynamics

1) A positively stable airplane will tend to pitch nosedown when power is reduced and controls are not adjusted. This is due to a number of factors.

   a) The airplane will tend to seek out the speed for which it is trimmed.

      i) In airplanes with a rear mounted horizontal stabilizer (or stabilator), the nose "stays up" due to a downward force produced by air flowing over the horizontal stabilizer, a feature inherent in that design.

      ii) With less power, the airplane will slow down.

      iii) The slower speed produces less airflow over the horizontal stabilizer.

      iv) The decreased airflow reduces the downward force on the horizontal stabilizer.

      v) The reduced downward force allows the nose to pitch down.

      vi) The nosedown pitch will tend to stabilize at an attitude that will attain the trimmed speed.

   b) In airplanes with a low horizontal stabilizer, a portion of the downward force on this surface is related to the airflow created by the air pushed over the surface by the propeller. The velocity of this air may be greater than the velocity of the airplane moving through the surrounding air under certain flight conditions. This additional airflow is not apparent in T-tail aircraft where the horizontal surface is above the "prop blast".

   c) An additional downward force may be created by the downwash of airflow from the top of the wings in airplanes with a low horizontal stabilizer. This is not apparent in T-tail aircraft.

   d) This phenomenon is also the subject of an FAA knowledge test question. The most correct answer for this question indicates that this also occurs because the downwash on the elevators from the propeller slipstream is reduced, decreasing elevator effectiveness.

2) **Torque** effect is greatest in a single-engine airplane at low airspeed, high power, and high angle of attack.

3) The indicated airspeed at which a given airplane stalls does not change with altitude as long as its weight, load factor, and configuration remain the same.

4) With regard to **wingtip vortices**, a light, quartering tailwind requires maximum caution on takeoff or landing because wind moves the vortices down the runway.

Volume 3 - Your First Solo

Aerodynamics

1) The amount of excess load that can be imposed on the wing of an airplane depends upon the **speed** of the airplane.

2) Upon encountering severe turbulence, a pilot should attempt to maintain a level flight attitude that will keep the airplane at or below **maneuvering speed**.

3) The most important rule to remember in the event of a power failure after becoming airborne is to immediately establish the proper gliding attitude and airspeed. Fly the airplane!

Weather Theory

1) Clouds, fog, or dew will always form when water vapor condenses.

2) **Evaporation** and **sublimation** are processes by which moisture is added to unsaturated air.

3) Fog

  a) Advection fog and **upslope fog** depend upon wind in order to exist.

  b) Low level turbulence can occur and icing can become hazardous in **steam fog**.

Weather Data

1) **Aviation Routine Weather Report**, or **METAR** report, is an actual observation taken from the surface of the airport every hour. If rapid changes occur in the weather, special report observations are taken. METARs will contain any of the following information that is pertinent to the observation:

  a) Type of Report -- METAR or SPECI (special).

  b) Station Designator -- ICAO identifier.

  c) Time of Report -- Reported in UTC.

  d) Wind Information -- Direction in tens of degrees from true north and wind speed in knots.

  e) Visibility -- Reported in statute miles; may also include Runway Visual Range (RVR) for a particular runway in feet.

  f) Weather and Obstructions to Visibility.

  g) Sky Condition -- Height of ceiling and other layers, and amount of coverage of layers.

  h) Temperature and Dew Point -- Reported in degrees Celsius.

  i) Altimeter Setting -- Given in inches of mercury.

  j) Remarks -- Any significant data not reported above.

2) The hourly METAR for KJFK airport in New York is decoded for you below:

METAR –Aviation Routine Weather Report

METAR KINK 121845Z 11012G18KT 15SM SKC 25/17 A3000
METAR KBOI 121854Z 13004KT 30SM SCT150 17/6 A3015
METAR KLAX 121852Z 25004KT 6SM BR SCT007 SCT250 16/15 A2991
SPECI KMDW 121856Z 32005KT 1 1/2SM RA OVC007 17/16 A2980 RMK RAB35
SPECI KJFK 121853Z 18004KT 1/2SM FG R04R/2200FT OVC005 20/18 A3006

  a) The full KJFK report reads:

  i) Special observation; 12th day of the month; time of observation 1853 (Zulu); wind direction 180° true, velocity 4 knots; 1/2 statute mile visibility in fog; Runway 4 Right visual range is 2,200 feet; ceiling 500 overcast; temperature 20°C, dew point 18°C; altimeter setting 30.06 inches.

3) Utilize **Terminal Aerodrome Forecasts** for information regarding expected weather at the time of arrival at your destination. Terminal Aerodrome Forecasts, or **TAF**s, predict weather conditions expected within 5 statute miles (SM) of the airport or "aerodrome". Use of the code "VC" (vicinity) applies to weather conditions expected to occur from between 5 to 10 SM from the airport. TAFs are issued four times daily and usually cover a 24-hour period.

4) The **Terminal Aerodrome Forecast** for KOKC can be read below:

TAF – Terminal Aerodrome Forecast

> **KOKC 051130Z 051212 14008KT 5SM BR BKN030 TEMPO 1316 1 1/2SM BR FM 1600 16010KT P6SM NSW SKC BECMG 2224 20013G20KT 4SM SHRA OVC020 PROB40 0006 2SM TSRA OVC008CB BECMG 0608 21015KT P6SM NSW SCT040=**

   a) The complete KOKC TAF reads: "**051130Z**" the first 2-digit pair represents the day of the month (in this case, the 5th), the next 4 digits indicate that the forecast was issued at **1130Z**. "**051212**" indicates that the TAF is valid from **12**00Z on the **5**th through **12**00Z on the sixth. The weather then begins wind **140°** at **08** KnoTs, visibility **5** Statute Miles in mist (**BR**) with a (**0**)**3,0**00 foot BroKeN ceiling. **TEMPO**rarily (generally less than an hour total and less than half of the forecast time period) between **13**00Z and **16**00Z, the visibility is expected to drop to 1 and 1/2 miles in mist (BR). FroM (after) **16**00Z, the wind is expected to be **160°** at **10** KnoTs, visibility Plus (greater than) **6** Statute Miles with No Significant Weather and SKy Clear. **BECoMinG** between **22**00Z and **24**00Z, wind **200°** at **13** Gusting to **20** KnoTs, visibility **4** Statute Miles in RAin SHowers with a ceiling of (**0**)**2,0**00 OVerCast. There is a **40%** PROBability that between **00**00Z and **06**00Z, the visibility will be **2** Statute Miles in ThunderStorms with RAin and a ceiling of (**00**)**,8**00 feet OVerCast with CumulonimBus clouds. **BECoMinG** between **06**00Z and **08**00Z, wind **210°** at **15** KnoTs, visibility Plus (greater than) **6** Statute Miles with No Significant Weather and SCaTtered clouds at (**0**)**4,0**00 feet. "=" signifies the end of the forecast data.

5) **Weather Depiction Charts** are valuable for determining general weather conditions for flight planning. Weather Depiction Charts are computer prepared from METARs to give a broad overview of observed weather at the valid time of the chart.

6) **Radar Summary Charts** show lines and areas of precipitation and thunderstorms. Weather radar cannot detect ceilings, fog, or clouds.

7) Weather Briefings

   a) When requesting a briefing, you should identify yourself as a pilot, that you are flying VFR, and give clear and concise facts about your flight:

i) Aircraft identification or pilot's name	v) Flight altitude(s)
ii) Aircraft type	vi) Route of flight
iii) Departure point	vii) Destination
iv) Proposed time of departure	viii) Estimated time en route (ETE)

   b) A complete weather briefing calls for a **standard briefing**. If no preliminary weather information has been received, request a standard briefing.

   c) To supplement mass disseminated data, request an **abbreviated briefing**. To update a previous weather briefing, request an abbreviated briefing.

   d) An **outlook briefing** should be requested when the estimated time of departure is six or more hours away.

Aircraft Instruments

1) Prior to takeoff, the altimeter should be set to the current local altimeter setting, if available, or the known elevation of the departure airport.

   a) Altimeter setting is the value to which the barometric pressure scale of the altimeter is set so the altimeter indicates true altitude at field elevation.

   b) Pressure levels are raised on warm days and the indicated altitude is lower than true altitude.

      i) This is referring to a vertical raising of the pressure levels, NOT an increase in pressure.

2) If the static vents become clogged, the altimeter and vertical speed indicator will become inoperative while the airspeed indicator will be inoperative in the sense that it is no longer accurate after you change altitudes. If the pitot tube becomes clogged, the airspeed indicator alone will become inoperative.

Aeromedical

1) Large accumulations of **carbon monoxide** in the human body result in loss of muscle power and can lead to unconsciousness. Susceptibility to carbon monoxide poisoning increases as altitude increases.

Federal Aviation Regulations

Certification Categories vs. Classes

Type of Certification	Category Examples	Class Examples
With respect to the certification of **Airmen**	Airplane, Rotorcraft, Glider, Lighter-Than-Air, Powered-Lift	Single-Engine Land, Single-Engine Sea, Multiengine Land, Multiengine Sea
With respect to the certification of **Aircraft**	Normal, Utility, Acrobatic	Airplane, Helicopter, Glider, Hot Air Balloon

Collision Avoidance

1) Prior to starting each maneuver, pilots should visually scan the entire area for collision avoidance.

2) Haze causes all traffic and terrain features to appear to be farther away than their actual distance.

Light Signals

Color and Type of Signal	On the Ground	In Flight
STEADY GREEN	Cleared for takeoff	Cleared to land
FLASHING GREEN	Cleared to taxi	Return for landing (to be followed by steady green at proper time)
STEADY RED	Stop	Give way to other aircraft and continue circling
FLASHING RED	Taxi clear of landing area (runway) in use	Airport unsafe--do not land
FLASHING WHITE	Return to starting point on airport	
ALTERNATING RED & GREEN	General Warning Signal--Exercise Extreme Caution	

Volume 5 - Your Dual Cross-Countries

Airport Lighting & Marking

1) Airport taxiway edge lights are identified at night by **blue omnidirectional lights**.

2) An airport's rotating beacon operating during daylight hours indicates that weather in **Class B, C & D airspace** and **Class E airspace designated for an airport** is below basic VFR weather minimums.

3) At airports without an operating control tower, a segmented circle, if installed, is designed to provide traffic pattern information. Unless otherwise indicated, the traffic pattern will be flown using turns to the left. If there is a variation to the normal left-hand traffic pattern, traffic pattern indicators will be used to indicate direction of turns.

4) The Airport Diagram to the right, illustrates runway orientation and shows a segmented circle with a tetrahedron wind indicator.

Airport Diagram

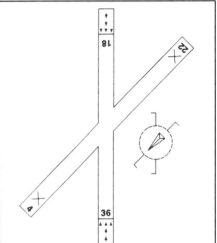

    a) The segmented circle indicates that there is right hand traffic for Runway 18 and there is left hand traffic for Runway 36. Runway 4-22 is closed as indicated by the "X" at the approach end of each runway. Runways 18-36 have displaced thresholds. The "threshold" is the beginning of the runway available and suitable for the landing of the aircraft. A "displaced threshold" is not at the beginning of the runway pavement, but located down the runway.

Collision Avoidance

1) The most effective way to use the eyes during night flight is to scan slowly to permit off-center viewing.

Publications

1) The Common Traffic Advisory Frequency (CTAF) may be a tower frequency (while tower not in operation), an **FSS frequency, UNICOM, or MULTICOM**.

    a) UNICOM is a non-government communication facility to provide airport information at certain airports. Unless otherwise indicated, 122.8 is the standard Unicom frequency.

    b) MULTICOM is a mobile service to conduct activities by or directed from private aircraft, standard frequency is 122.9 for airports with no control tower, FSS, or UNICOM and is122.95 for those with a control tower or FSS.

2) The correct method of stating 4,500 feet MSL to ATC is "Four Thousand Five Hundred."

3) If flying HAWK N666CB, the proper phraseology for initial contact with McAlester FSS is "McAlester Radio, Hawk Six Six Six Charlie Bravo, receiving Ardmore VORTAC, over."

4) FAA Advisory Circulars contain information of a non-regulatory nature, but of interest to pilots.

    a) Advisory Circulars containing matter covering the subject of Airmen are issued under subject number **60**.

    b) Advisory Circulars containing matter covering the subject of Airspace are issued under subject number **70**.

    c) Advisory Circulars containing matter covering the subjects of Air Traffic Control and General Operating Rules are issued under subject number **90**.

Navigation

1) Tabulations of parachute jump areas in the U.S. are contained in the Airport/Facility Directory (A/FD).

2) An A/FD listing for an airport including "**VHF/DF**" indicates FAA facilities located at the airport have Very High Frequency Direction Finding equipment. The VHF/DF equipment shows the magnetic direction of the aircraft from the ground station each time the aircraft transmits. This capability is used to locate lost aircraft.

3) To use VHF/DF facilities for assistance in locating an aircraft's position, the aircraft must have a VHF transmitter and receiver.

VOR Navigation

1) VORs "G", "H", and "I" below illustrate common VOR indications.

VOR – Very High Frequency Omnidirectional Range.

G

a) VOR G: The OBS is set on 210° with a right CDI deflection and no TO or FROM indication. This means the aircraft is abeam of the facility on the 120-300° line through the station or the 120° radial.

H

b) VOR H: The OBS is set on 210°, with a TO indication. The course, if flown, would take the aircraft to the station.

I

c) VOR I: The OBS is set on 210°, with a FROM indication. The course, if flown, would take the aircraft away from the station on the 210° radial.

ADF Navigation

1) Here is a frequently used formula that calculates the answers to several ADF type problems:

a) Magnetic Heading + Relative Bearing = Magnetic Bearing to the station. **MH + RB = MB**

Weather Data

1) A **PIREP** is a Pilot Weather Report. An example of a PIREP is shown and explained below:

PIREP – Pilot Weather Report

> **UA/OV KOKC-KTUL/TM 1800/FL120/TP BE90/SK BKN018-TOP055/OVC072-**
> **TOP089/CLR ABV/TA M7/WV 08021/TB LGT 055-072/IC LGT-MOD RIME 072-089**

   a) This is a (UA) PIREP from an aircraft (/OV KOKC-KTUL) between Oklahoma City and Tulsa at (/TM 1800) 1800 UTC, altitude (/FL 120) 12,000 feet MSL, type of aircraft (/TP BE90) is a Beech 90. The aircraft reports (/SK BKN018-TOP055/OVC072-TOP089/CLR ABV) bases of broken clouds at 1,800 MSL with tops of that layer at 5,500 feet MSL, base of a second layer of clouds which are overcast is at 7,200 feet MSL, tops at 8,900 MSL, clear above. The temperature is (/TA M7) minus 7° Celsius, and the wind is (/WV 08021) 080° at 21 knots. This aircraft reported (/TB LGT 055-072) light turbulence existed between 5,500 feet MSL and 7,200 feet MSL along with (/IC LGT-MOD RIME 072-089) light to moderate rime icing between 7,200 feet MSL and 8,900 feet MSL.

Airspace

1) There are **four** broad divisions of airspace. They are **Controlled, Uncontrolled, Special Use,** and **Other** airspace.

2) **Controlled** airspace is supported by air navigation aids, ground to air communication, and air traffic control services. **Controlled** airspace consists of **Class A, B, C, D,** and **E** airspace.

3) The United States does not have any airspace equivalent to the International Civil Aviation Organization's (ICAO) Class F.

4) **Class G** is uncontrolled airspace where ATC has neither the authority nor the responsibility for controlling aircraft.

5) **Special Use Airspace** consists of Prohibited, Restricted, Warning, Military Operations, Alert, and Controlled Firing Areas.

   a) **Prohibited Areas** specifically prohibit aircraft flight.

   b) **Restricted Areas** are defined as airspace where aircraft flight is subject to restrictions.

      i) Pilots may fly through a restricted area with the controlling agency's authorization.

   c) **Warning Areas** are in international airspace. Activities in Warning Areas may be hazardous to non-participating aircraft.

      i) Unusual, often invisible hazards such as aerial gunnery or guided missiles over international waters may exist in Warning Areas.

   d) **Military Operations Areas** (MOAs) are segments of airspace defined by vertical and lateral limits used to segregate military training activities from aircraft operating under IFR.

      i) High-density military training activities may exist in MOAs.

      ii) When operating under VFR in a MOA, a pilot should exercise extreme caution when military activity is being conducted.

   e) **Alert Areas** are depicted on charts to warn pilots of a high volume of pilot training or other unusual aerial activity.

      i) Responsibility for collision avoidance in an alert area rests with **all pilots**.

   f) **Controlled Firing Areas** have activities that, if not controlled, would be hazardous to non-participating aircraft.

      i) Activities are suspended immediately when spotter aircraft, radar, or ground lookout positions indicate an aircraft might be approaching the area.

6) **Other Airspace** designations <u>are not airspace classifications</u> but could be **within** any of the classes of airspace.

    a) An **Airport Advisory Area** is the area within 10 statute miles of an airport where an FSS is located and a control tower is not operating.

        i) Prior to entering an Airport Advisory Area, a pilot should contact the local FSS for airport and traffic advisories.

    b) **Military Training Routes** (MTRs) are mutually developed by the FAA and the Department of Defense.

        i) MTRs designated "IR" indicate a route to be flown IFR regardless of weather. "VR" routes are to be flown VFR and only with a visibility and ceiling greater than 5 miles and 3000 feet, respectively.

        ii) A 3-digit number identifies a route with one or more segments above 1,500 feet AGL, and a 4-digit number identifies a route with all segments below 1,500 AGL.

    c) **Terminal Radar Service Areas (TRSAs)** are established to provide radar separation of participating VFR aircraft and all aircraft operating under Instrument Flight Rules.

        i) Stage III service in the terminal radar program provides sequencing and separation for participating VFR aircraft. Participation is not mandatory.

        ii) Prior to entering a **TRSA**, a pilot should contact approach control on the appropriate frequency if radar traffic information is desired.

        iii) **TRSA**s are depicted on charts with a **solid black line**.

        iv) **TRSA**s, as entities, **are not** an airspace class.

7) Transponders

    a) An operable transponder with Mode C (an encoding altimeter) is required:

        i) In **Class A, B,** and **C** airspace.

        ii) Within 30 miles of a **Class B** primary airport from the surface upward to 10,000 ft. MSL, with certain exceptions.

        iii) In all airspace above the ceiling and within the lateral boundaries of a **Class B** or **Class C** airspace area designated for an airport upward to 10,000 ft. MSL.

        iv) In all airspace of the 48 contiguous states and the District of Columbia at and above 10,000 feet MSL, excluding the airspace at and below 2,500 feet above the surface.

Controlled and Uncontrolled Airspace Classifications

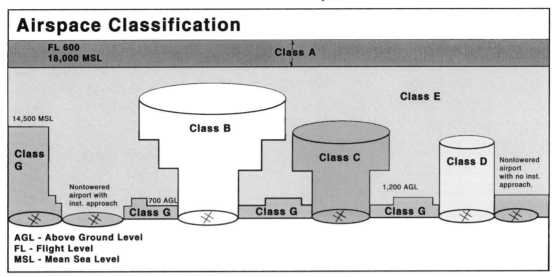

AGL - Above Ground Level
FL - Flight Level
MSL - Mean Sea Level

Airspace	Class A	Class B	Class C	Class D	Class E	Class G
Entry Requirements	IFR clearance	ATC clearance	Prior two-way communications	Prior two-way communications	None	None
Minimum Pilot Qualifications	Instrument Rating	Private or Student certification. Local restrictions apply	Student certificate	Student certificate	Student certificate	Student certificate
Two-Way Radio Communications	Yes	Yes	Yes	Yes	Not required	Not required
Special VFR Allowed	No	Yes	Yes	Yes	Yes	N/A
VFR Visibility Minimum	N/A	3 statute miles	3 statute miles	3 statute miles	3 statute miles*	1 statute mile**
VFR Minimum Distance from Clouds	N/A	Clear of clouds	500' below, 1,000' above, 2,000' horizontal	500' below, 1,000' above, 2,000' horizontal	500' below,* 1,000' above, 2,000' horizontal	Clear of clouds**
VFR Aircraft Separation	N/A	All	IFR aircraft	Runway Operations	None	None
Traffic Advisories	Yes	Yes	Yes	Workload permitting	Workload permitting	Workload permitting
Airport Application	N/A	•Radar •Instrument Approaches •Weather •Control Tower •High Density	•Radar •Instrument Approaches •Weather •Control Tower	•Instrument Approaches •Weather •Control Tower	•Instrument Approaches •Weather	

*Only true below 10,000 feet.
**Only true during day at or below 1,200 feet AGL (see 14 CFR part 91).

Volume 6 - Your Solo Cross-Countries

Aircraft Performance

1) Propeller efficiency is directly related to the amount of air it accelerates. In other words, less air, less propulsion.

   a) High density altitude reduces propeller efficiency because the propeller exerts less force at high density altitudes than at low density altitudes.

2) Fewer air molecules at a given level in the atmosphere due to warmer than standard temperatures, lower than standard pressures, or higher humidity, will cause density altitude to be higher.

Weather Theory

1) Icing

   a) Conditions necessary for structural icing to form are:

      i) Visible moisture.

      ii) Temperature below freezing at the point of impact.

   b) Aircraft structural ice is most likely to have the highest accumulation rate in freezing rain.

2) Stability

   a) Warming from below will decrease the stability of an air mass.

3) Clouds

   a) The suffix nimbus, used in naming clouds, means a rain cloud.

   b) Cumulonimbus clouds have the greatest turbulence.

4) General

   a) Thunderstorms are obscured by massive cloud layers when a current SIGMET forecasts embedded thunderstorms.

   b) Possible mountain wave turbulence can be anticipated when winds of 40 knots or greater blow across a mountain ridge, and the air is stable.

Volume 7 - Your Private Pilot Test

Federal Aviation Regulations

1) No person may operate an aircraft that has an experimental certificate along a congested airway (unless otherwise specifically authorized).

Page Intentionally Left Blank

Section 3 - Appendices and Supplemental Material

Appendix A – Airworthiness Requirements for VFR Flight

1) The following instruments and equipment are required for a flight in an airplane under day VFR conditions:
   a) Airspeed indicator.
   b) Altimeter.
   c) Magnetic direction indicator.
   d) Tachometer for each engine.
   e) Oil pressure gauge for each engine using a pressure system.
   f) Temperature gauge for each liquid-cooled engine.
   g) Oil temperature gauge for each air-cooled engine.
   h) Manifold pressure gauge for each altitude engine.
   i) Fuel gauge indicating the quantity of fuel in each tank.
   j) Landing gear position indicator, if the aircraft has a retractable landing gear.
   k) For small civil airplanes certificated after March 11, 1996, an approved aviation red or aviation white anticollision light system.
   l) If the aircraft is operated for hire over water and beyond power-off gliding distance from shore, approved flotation gear readily available to each occupant and at least one pyrotechnic signaling device.
   m) An approved safety belt with an approved metal-to-metal latching device for each occupant 2 years of age or older.
   n) For small civil airplanes manufactured after July 18, 1978, an approved shoulder harness for each front seat.
   o) An emergency locator transmitter, if required by 14 CFR Section 91.207.
   p) For normal, utility, and acrobatic category airplanes with a seating configuration, excluding pilot seats, of 9 or less, manufactured after December 12, 1986, a shoulder harness for all forward or aft facing seats. Seats facing other directions must afford the same level of protection.

2) The following instruments and equipment are required for a flight in an airplane under night VFR conditions:
   a) All equipment and instruments required for day VFR.
   b) Approved position lights.
   c) An approved aviation red or aviation white anticollision light system.
   d) If the aircraft is operated for hire, one electric landing light.
   e) An adequate source of electrical energy for all installed electrical and radio equipment.
   f) One spare set of fuses, or three spare fuses of each kind required, that are accessible to the pilot in flight.

3) When an airplane has inoperative equipment, the pilot's required actions will differ depending on whether or not the aircraft has an approved Minimum Equipment List (MEL) and letter of authorization.
   a) The letter of authorization is issued by the FAA Flight Standards district office having jurisdiction over the area in which the operator is located and authorizes operation of the aircraft under the MEL. The MEL and the letter of authorization constitute a supplemental type certificate for the aircraft and must be in the airplane.
   b) If an airplane has an approved MEL, the aircraft must be operated in accordance with the provisions of the MEL.

4) If no Minimum Equipment List is available and the airplane is small and not turbine powered, the pilot may elect to conduct the operation with the inoperative equipment under certain conditions.

    a) The inoperative instruments and equipment must not:

        i) Be required by the airworthiness regulations under which the aircraft was type certificated.

        ii) Be indicated as required on the aircraft's equipment list, or on the Kinds of Operations Equipment List for the kind of flight operation being conducted.

        iii) Be required by 14 CFR Section 91.205 or any other rule for the specific kind of flight operation being conducted.

        iv) Be required to be operational by an airworthiness directive.

        v) Constitute a hazard to the aircraft as determined by a pilot, who is certificated and appropriately rated under 14 CFR Part 61, or by a person, who is certificated and appropriately rated to perform maintenance on the aircraft.

    b) The inoperative instruments and equipment must be handled in one of the following ways:

        i) It must be removed from the aircraft, the cockpit control placarded, and the maintenance recorded in accordance with applicable regulations.

        ii) It must be deactivated and placarded "Inoperative." If deactivation of the inoperative instrument or equipment involves maintenance, it must be accomplished and recorded in accordance with applicable regulations.

        iii) Though generally required for VFR operations, operation of the aircraft may continue to a location where repairs or replacement can be made for the failure of any light of the anticollision light system.

5) A special flight permit may be issued for an aircraft that may not currently meet applicable airworthiness requirements but is capable of safe flight, for the following purposes:

    a) Flying the aircraft to a base where repairs, alterations, or maintenance are to be performed, or to a point of storage.

    b) Delivering or exporting the aircraft.

    c) Production flight testing new production aircraft.

    d) Evacuating aircraft from areas of impending danger.

    e) Conducting customer demonstration flights in new production aircraft that have satisfactorily completed production flight tests.

6) A special flight permit may also be issued to authorize the operation of an aircraft at a weight in excess of its maximum certificated takeoff weight for flight beyond the normal range over water, or over land areas where adequate landing facilities or appropriate fuel is not available. The excess weight that may be authorized under this paragraph is limited to the additional fuel, fuel-carrying facilities, and navigation equipment necessary for the flight.

7) The issuance of a special flight permit requires an applicant to submit a statement in a manner acceptable to the FAA Administrator with the following information:

    a) The purpose of the flight.

    b) The proposed itinerary.

    c) The crew required to operate the aircraft and its equipment.

    d) The ways, if any, in which the aircraft does not comply with the applicable airworthiness requirements.

    e) Any restriction the applicant considers necessary for safe operation of the aircraft.

    f) Any other information considered necessary by the Administrator for the purpose of prescribing operating limitations.

8) The Administrator may make, or require the applicant to make appropriate inspections or tests necessary for safety.

9) Airworthiness Directives (ADs) are regulatory notices issued by the FAA requiring the correction or prevention of an unsafe condition found in an aircraft, aircraft engine, propeller, or appliance.

    a) The unsafe condition may be the result of a design defect, a maintenance issue, or other causes.

    b) 14 CFR Part 39 defines the authority and responsibility of the FAA Administrator with regard to ADs.

    c) ADs must be complied with unless a specific exemption is received from the Administrator.

    d) The aircraft owner or operator is responsible for ensuring compliance with applicable ADs.

10) ADs may be divided into two categories:

    a) Those of an emergency nature requiring immediate compliance.

    b) Those of a less urgent nature requiring compliance within a specified period of time.

11) The regulations require that a record be maintained showing the current status of the applicable ADs. This record must include:

    a) The method of compliance.

    b) The signature and certificate number of the repair station or mechanic who performed the work.

    c) This record is typically found in the aircraft logbooks.

12) A summary of the valid Airworthiness Directives is available from the FAA.

Appendix B – Additional Weather Information

1) Surface Analysis Chart

    a) The surface analysis chart is a computer-generated chart, with frontal analysis by forecasters from the Hydrometeorolgical Prediction Center (HPC) in Camp Springs, Maryland.

    b) It is transmitted every 3 hours and covers the contiguous 48 states and adjacent areas.

    c) The surface analysis chart provides a ready means of locating pressure systems and fronts and it gives an overview of winds, temperatures, and dew point temperatures at chart time.

    d) Keep in mind that this chart is historical in nature and shows the conditions at the time the chart was created.

    e) Use the surface analysis chart in conjunction with other information to give a more complete weather picture.

Sky Cover Symbols

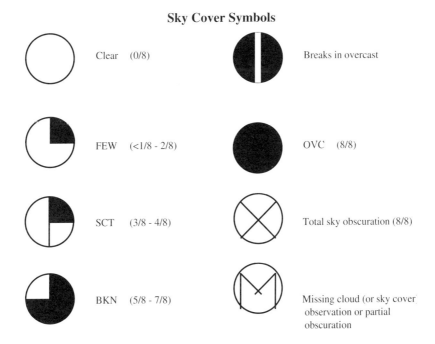

Clear (0/8)	Breaks in overcast
FEW (<1/8 - 2/8)	OVC (8/8)
SCT (3/8 - 4/8)	Total sky obscuration (8/8)
BKN (5/8 - 7/8)	Missing cloud (or sky cover observation or partial obscuration)

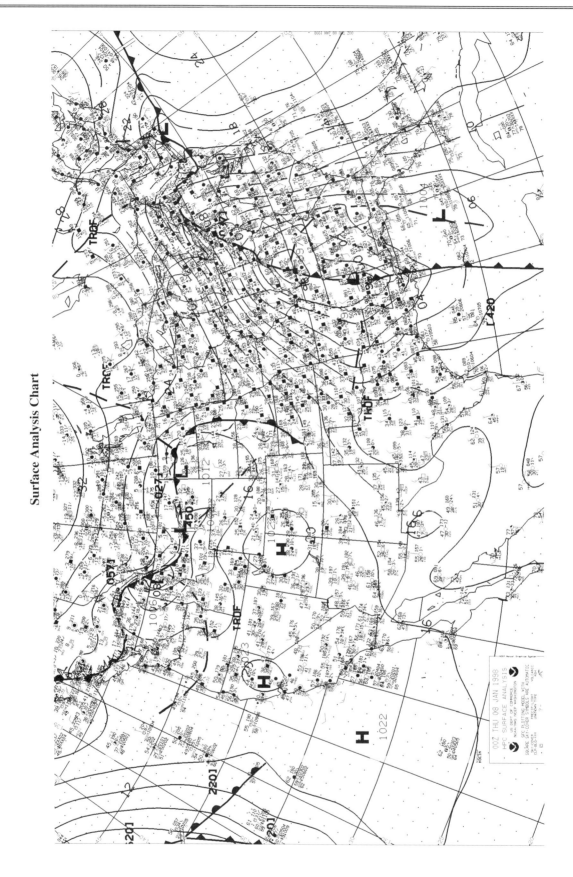

Surface Analysis Chart

Symbols on Surface Analysis Chart

Color	Symbol	Description
Blue	H	High Pressure Center
Red	L	Low Pressure Center
Blue		Cold Front
Red		Warm Front
Red/Blue		Stationary Front
Purple		Occluded Front
Blue		Cold Frontogenesis
Red		Warm Frontogenesis
Red/Blue		Stationary Frontogenesis
Blue		Cold Frontolysis
Red		Warm Frontolysis
Red/Blue		Stationary Frontolysis
Purple		Occluded Frontolysis
Purple		Squall Line
Brown		Dryline
Brown		Trough
Yellow		Ridge

Station Model and Explanation

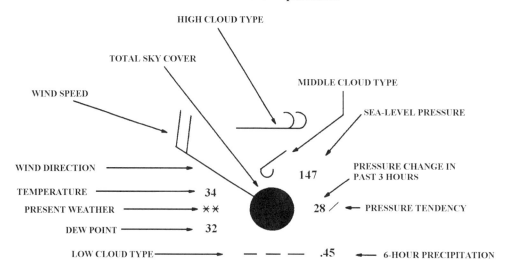

1. **Total sky cover: Overcast.**
2. **Temperature: 34 degrees F, Dew Point: 32 degrees F.**
3. **Wind: From the northwest at 20 knots (relative to true north).**

Examples of wind direction and speed

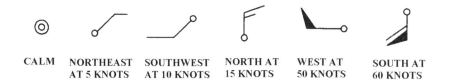

| CALM | NORTHEAST AT 5 KNOTS | SOUTHWEST AT 10 KNOTS | NORTH AT 15 KNOTS | WEST AT 50 KNOTS | SOUTH AT 60 KNOTS |

4. **Present Weather: Continuous light snow.**
5. **Predominate low, middle, high cloud reported: Strato fractus or cumulus fractus of bad weather, altocumulus in patches, and dense cirrus.**
6. **Sea-level pressure: 1,014.7 millibars (mbs).**
   NOTE: Pressure is always shown in three digits to nearest tenth of an mb. For 1,000 mbs or greater, prefix a "10" to the three digits. For less than 1,000 mbs, prefix a "9" to the three digits.
7. **Pressure change in the past 3 hours: Increased steadily or unsteadily by 2.8 mbs. The actual change is in tenths of a mb.**
8. **6 - hour precipitation in hundredths of an inch: 45 hundredths of an inch.**

Type of Front

Code Figures	Descriptions
0	Quasi-stationary at surface
2	Warm front at surface
4	Cold front at surface
6	Occlusion
7	Instability line

Intensity of Front

Code Figures	Descriptions
0	No specification
1	Weak, decreasing
2	Weak, little, or no change
3	Weak, increasing
4	Moderate, decreasing
5	Moderate, little, or no change
6	Moderate, increasing
7	Strong, decreasing
8	Strong, little, or no change
9	Strong, increasing

Character of Front

Code Figures	Descriptions
0	No specification
5	Forming or existence expected
6	Quasi-stationary
7	With waves
8	Diffuse

Pressure Tendencies

Description of Characteristic			
Primary Requirements	**Additional Requirements**	**Graphic**	**Code Figure**
Higher Atmospheric pressure now higher than 3 hours ago.	Increasing, then decreasing	/\	0
	Increasing, then steady; or Increasing, then increasing more slowly	/ ‾	1
	Increasing; steadily or unsteadily	/	2
	Decreasing; or steady, then increasing; or Increasing, then increasing more rapidly	√	3
	Increasing, then decreasing	/\	0
Same Atmospheric pressure now same as 3 hours ago.	Steady	—	4
	Decreasing, then increasing	\/	5
Lower Atmospheric pressure now lower than 3 hours ago.	Decreasing, then increasing	\/	5
	Decreasing, then steady; or Decreasing, then decreasing more slowly	_	6
	Decreasing; steadily or unsteadily	\	7
	Steady; or increasing, then decreasing; or Decreasing, then decreasing more rapidly	/\	8

Present Weather Symbols

	0	1	2	3	4	5	6	7	8	9
00	Cloud development NOT observed or NOT observable during past hour.	Clouds generally dissolving or becoming less developed during past hour.	State of the sky on the whole unchanged during past hour.	Clouds generally forming or developing during past hour.	Visibility reduced by smoke.	Visibility reduced by haze.	Widespread dust in suspension in the air, NOT raised by the wind at time of observation.	Dust or sand raised by wind at time of observation.	Well developed dust devil(s) within past hour.	Dust storm or sandstorm within sight of or at station during past hour.
10	Light fog.	Patches of shallow fog at station, NOT deeper than 6 feet on land.	More or less continuous shallow fog at station, NOT deeper than 6 feet on land.	Lightning visible, no thunder heard.	Precipitation within sight, but NOT reaching the ground.	Precipitation within sight, reaching the ground but distant from station.	Precipitation within sight, reaching the ground near to but NOT at station.	Thunder heard, but no precipitation at the station.	Squall(s) within sight during past hour.	Funnel cloud(s) within sight during past hour.
20	Drizzle (NOT freezing and NOT falling as showers) during past hour, but NOT at time of observation.	Rain (NOT freezing and NOT falling as showers) during past hour, but NOT at time of observation.	Snow (NOT falling as showers) during past hour, but NOT at time of observation.	Rain and snow (NOT falling as showers) during past hour, but NOT at time of observation.	Freezing drizzle or freezing rain (NOT falling as showers) during past hour, but NOT at time of observation.	Showers of rain during past hour, but NOT at time of observation.	Showers of snow, or of rain and snow, during past hour, but NOT at time of observation.	Showers of hail, or of hail and rain, during past hour, but NOT at time of observation.	Fog during past hour, but NOT at time of observation.	Thunderstorm (with or without precipitation) during past hour, but NOT at time of observation.
30	Slight or moderate dust storm or sandstorm, has decreased during past hour.	Slight or moderate dust storm or sandstorm, no appreciable change during past hour.	Slight or moderate dust storm or sandstorm, has increased during past hour.	Severe dust storm or sandstorm, has decreased during past hour.	Severe dust storm or sandstorm, no appreciable change during past hour.	Severe dust storm or sandstorm, has increased during past hour.	Slight or moderate drifting snow, generally low.	Heavy drifting snow, generally low.	Slight or moderate drifting snow, generally high.	Heavy drifting snow, generally high.
40	Fog at distance at time of observation, but NOT at station during past hour.	Fog in patches.	Fog, sky discernible, has become thinner during past hour.	Fog, sky NOT discernible, has become thinner during past hour.	Fog, sky discernible, no appreciable change during past hour.	Fog, sky NOT discernible, no appreciable change during past hour.	Fog, sky discernible, has begun or become thicker during past hour.	Fog, sky NOT discernible, has begun or become thicker during past hour.	Fog, depositing rime, sky discernible.	Fog, depositing rime, sky NOT discernible.
50	Intermittent drizzle (NOT freezing), slight at time of observation.	Continuous drizzle (NOT freezing), slight at time of observation.	Intermittent drizzle (NOT freezing), moderate at time of observation.	Continuous drizzle (NOT freezing), moderate at time of observation.	Intermittent drizzle (NOT freezing), thick, at time of observation.	Continuous drizzle (NOT freezing), thick, at time of observation.	Slight freezing drizzle.	Moderate or thick freezing drizzle.	Drizzle and rain, slight.	Drizzle and rain, moderate or heavy.
60	Intermittent rain (NOT freezing), slight at time of observation.	Continuous rain, (NOT freezing), slight at time of observation.	Intermittent rain (NOT freezing), moderate at time of observation.	Continuous rain (NOT freezing), moderate at time of observation.	Intermittent rain, (NOT freezing), heavy at time of observation.	Continuous rain, (NOT freezing), heavy at time of observation.	Slight freezing rain.	Moderate or heavy freezing rain.	Rain or drizzle and snow, slight.	Rain or drizzle and snow, moderate or heavy.
70	Intermittent fall of snowflakes, slight at time of observation.	Continuous fall of snowflakes, slight at time of observation.	Intermittent fall of snowflakes, moderate at time of observation.	Continuous fall of snowflakes, moderate at time of observation.	Intermittent fall of snowflakes, heavy at time of observation.	Continuous fall of snowflakes, heavy at time of observation.	Ice needles (with or without fog).	Granular snow (with or without fog).	Isolated starlike snow crystals (with or without fog).	Ice pellets (sleet, U.S. definition).
80	Slight rain shower(s).	Moderate or heavy rain shower(s).	Violent rain showers(s).	Slight showers(s) of rain and snow mixed.	Moderate or heavy showers(s) of rain and snow mixed.	Slight snow shower(s).	Moderate or heavy snow shower(s).	Slight shower(s) of soft or small hail with or without rain or rain and snow mixed.	Moderate or heavy shower(s) of soft or small hail with or without rain or rain and snow mixed.	Slight showers(s) of hail, with or without rain, or rain and snow mixed, NOT associated with thunder.
90	Moderate or heavy shower(s) of hail, with or without rain, or rain and snow mixed, NOT associated with thunder.	Slight rain at time of observation, thunderstorm during past hour, but NOT at time of observation.	Moderate or heavy rain at time of observation, thunderstorm during past hour, but NOT at time of observation.	Slight snow or rain and snow mixed or hail at time of observation, thunderstorm during past hour, but NOT at time of observation.	Moderate or heavy snow, or rain and snow mixed or hail at time of observation, thunderstorm during past hour, but NOT at time of observation.	Slight or moderate thunderstorm without hail but with rain and/or snow at time of observation.	Slight or moderate thunderstorm with hail at time of observation.	Heavy thunderstorm, without hail, but with rain and/or snow at time of observation.	Thunderstorm, combined with dust storm or sandstorm at time of observation.	Heavy thunderstorm, with hail at time of observation.

Cloud Symbols

CLOUD ABBREVIATION	C_L #	C_L DESCRIPTION (Abridged from W.M.O. Code)	C_M #	C_M DESCRIPTION (Abridged from W.M.O. Code)	C_H #	C_H DESCRIPTION (Abridged from W.M.O. Code)
St or Fs - Stratus or Fractostratus	1	Cu, fair weather, little vertical development and flattened	1	Thin As (most of cloud layer is semitransparent)	1	Filaments of Ci, or "mares tails," scattered and not increasing
Ci - Cirrus	2	Cu, considerable development, towering with or without other Cu or Sc bases at same level	2	Thick As, greater part sufficiently dense to hide sun (or moon), or Ns	2	Dense Ci in patches or twisted sheaves, usually not increasing, sometimes like remains of Cb; or towers tufts
Cs - Cirrostratus	3	Cb with tops lacking clearcut outlines, but distinctly not cirroform or anvil shaped; with or without Cu, Sc, or St	3	Thin Ac, mostly semitransparent; cloud elements not changing much at a single level	3	Dense Ci, often anvil shaped derived from or associated Cb
Cc - Cirrocumulus	4	Sc formed by spreading out of Cu; Cu often present also	4	Thin Ac in patches; cloud elements continually changing and/or occurring at more than one level	4	Ci, often hook shaped gradually spreading over the sky and usually thickening as a whole
Ac - Altocumulus	5	Sc not formed by spreading out of Cu	5	Thin Ac in bands or in a layer gradually spreading over sky and usually thickening as a whole	5	Ci and Cs, often in converging bands or Cs alone; generally overspreading and growing denser; the continuous layer not reaching 45 altitude
As - Altostratus	6	St or Fs or both, but no Fs of bad weather	6	Ac formed by the spreading out of Cu	6	Ci and Cs, often in converging bands or Cs alone; generally overspreading and growing denser; the continuous layer exceeding 45 altitude
Sc - Stratocumulus	7	Fs and/or Fc of bad weather (scud)	7	Double-layered Ac, or a thick layer of Ac, not increasing; or Ac with As and/or Ns	7	Veil of Cs covering the entire sky
Ns - Nimbostratus	8	Cu and Sc (not formed by spreading out of Cu) with bases at different levels	8	Ac in the form of Cu-shaped tufts or Ac with turrets	8	Cs not increasing and not covering the entire sky
Cu or Fc - Cumulus or Fractocumulus	9	Cb having a clearly fibrous (cirroform) top, often anvil shaped, with or without Cu, Sc, St, or scud	9	Ac of chaotic sky, usually at different levels; patches of dense Ci are usually present	9	Cc alone or Cc with some Ci or Cs but the Cc being the main cirroform cloud
Cb - Cumulonimbus						

2) Wind and Temperatures Aloft Charts

   a) The winds and temperatures aloft charts, both forecast and observed, are computer-generated products.

   b) Forecast winds and temperatures aloft (FD) charts are prepared for eight levels on eight separate panels.

      i) The levels are 6,000; 9,000; 12,000; 18,000; 24,000; 30,000; 34,000; and 39,000 feet MSL.

      ii) Levels below 18,000 feet are in true altitude, and levels 18,000 feet and above are in pressure altitude.

   c) The charts are available daily, and the 12-hour prognostics are valid at 1200Z and 0000Z.

   d) A legend on each panel shows the valid time and the level of the panel.

   e) Temperature is in whole degrees Celsius for each forecast point and is entered above and to the right of the station circle.

   f) Arrows with pennants and barbs, similar to those used on the surface map, show wind direction and speed.

      i) Wind direction is drawn to the nearest 10 degrees with the second digit of the coded direction entered at the outer end of the arrow.

      ii) To determine wind direction, obtain the general direction from the arrow, and then use the digit to determine the direction to the nearest 10 degrees.

      iii) A calm or light and variable wind is shown by "99" entered to the lower left of the station circle.

Plotted Winds and Temperatures

Plotted	Interpretation
	12 degrees Celsius, wind 060 degrees at 5 knots
	3 degrees Celsius, wind 160 degrees at 25 knots
	0 degrees Celsius, wind 250 degrees at 15 knots
	-9 degrees Celsius, wind 260 degrees at 50 knots
	-47 degrees Celsius, wind 360 degrees at 115 knots
	-11 degrees Celsius, wind calm or light and variable

Forecast Winds and Temperatures Aloft Chart

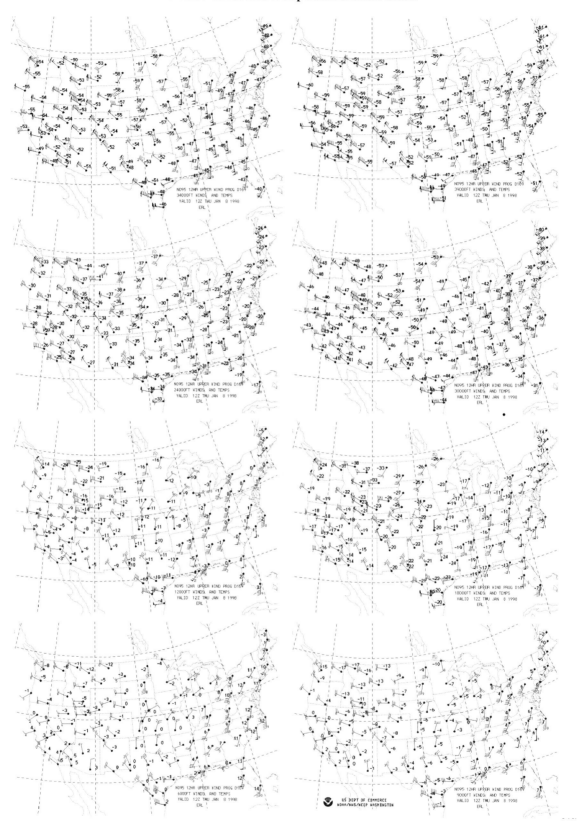

g)   Charts of observed winds for selected levels are sent twice daily on a four-panel chart valid at 1200Z and 0000Z.

h) The chart depicts winds at the second standard level, 14,000, 24,000, and 34,000 feet.

   i) The second standard level for a reporting station is found between 1,000 and 2,000 feet above the surface, depending on the station elevation.

   ii) The second standard level is used to determine low-level wind shear and frictional effects on lower atmosphere winds.

   iii) To compute the second standard level, find the next thousand-foot level above the station elevation and add 1,000 feet to that level.

i) Wind direction and speed are shown by arrows, the same as on the forecast charts.

   i) A calm or light and variable wind is shown as "LV" and a missing wind as "M," both plotted to the lower right of the station circle.

j) The station circle is filled in when the reported temperature/dew point spread is 5 degrees Celsius or less.

k) Observed temperatures are included on the 24,000 and 34,000 feet panels of this chart.

   i) A dotted bracket around the temperature means a calculated temperature.

Panel from Observed Winds and Temperatures Aloft Chart

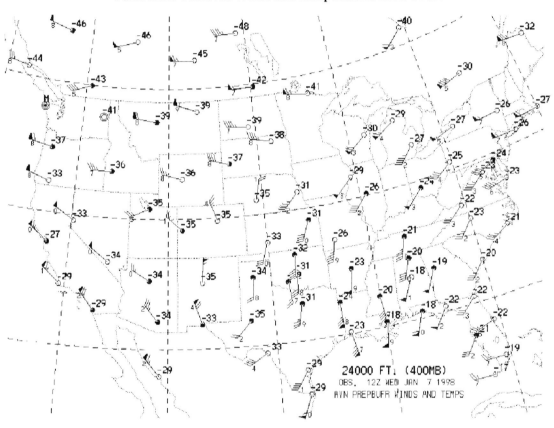

Observed Winds and Temperatures Aloft Chart

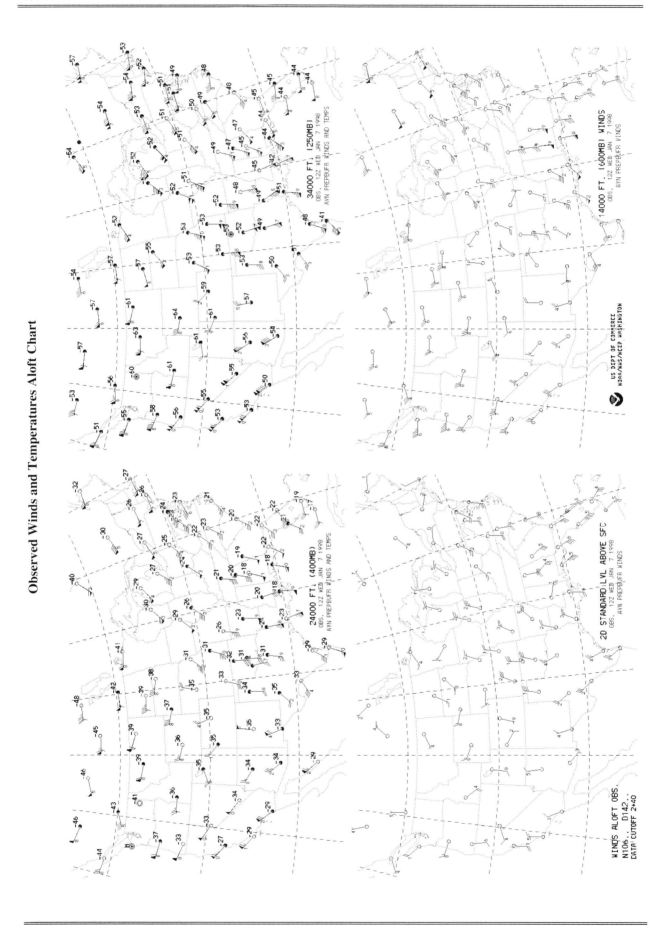

Appendix C – Motion Sickness and Dehydration

1) **Motion sickness** is caused by continued stimulation of the inner ear, which controls the sense of balance.

2) The symptoms are progressive. Pilots or passengers may experience:
   a) A loss of appetite.
   b) Saliva collecting in the mouth.
   c) Perspiration.
   d) Nausea / vomiting.
   e) Disorientation.
   f) Headaches.

3) If allowed to become severe, a pilot could become incapacitated.

4) When suffering from motion sickness:
   a) Open the air vents.
   b) Loosen clothing.
   c) Use oxygen if available.
   d) Try to focus on things outside of the airplane toward the horizon and minimize head movements.
   e) Terminate the flight as soon as practical.

5) A pilot should not use drugs intended to prevent motion sickness as they might have detrimental side effects.

6) **Dehydration** occurs when the human body does not get or retain the fluid it requires.
   a) Dehydration symptoms include:
      i) a feeling of thirst
      ii) dryness of the mouth, eyes, nose, and/or skin
      iii) headache
      iv) dizziness
      v) sleepiness
      vi) cramps
      vii) fatigue
   b) Prolonged dehydration can impair judgment and may lead to debilitating conditions.

7) Being in a hot and dry climate, breathing dry air or oxygen at altitude, being sick or sunburned, wearing improper clothing for hot conditions, eating salty foods, and the intake of diuretics such as drinks with caffeine or alcohol may contribute to the severity of dehydration.

8) Avoid dehydration while flying by drinking plenty of water, avoiding foods and drinks which promote the condition, and being dressed for the weather conditions.

Appendix D – Securing Loose Items

1) The cockpit and cabin should always be checked for loose articles during the preflight process. Loose articles can become projectiles or jam controls during turbulence or sudden aircraft movements.

2) Loose articles should be secured using appropriate tiedowns within the aircraft.
   a) Seatbelts in unoccupied seats may be useful for securing flight bags and other bulky articles. Be sure that these items are accounted for in the weight and balance and will not interfere with any controls even if they shift during flight.

Appendix E – Noise Abatement Procedures

1) Noise around airports has become a major concern at many locations around the country.

2) Noise abatement procedures have been developed at a large number of airports to help minimize noise for nearby sensitive areas.

3) These procedures are available from a number of sources within the aviation community and may include:

   a) Airport/Facility Directory.

   b) Local and regional publications.

   c) Printed handouts.

   d) Operator bulletin boards.

   e) Safety briefings.

   f) Local air traffic facilities.

4) Noise abatement reminder signs may be present along taxiways to encourage pilots to follow these procedures.

5) Even if noise abatement procedures are not in place, you should try to be a good neighbor and do your part to reduce or minimize the exposure to noise for individuals on the ground.

Appendix F – Determining Minimum Safe Altitude for Emergency Instrument Navigation

1) There are a number of considerations when determining the minimum safe altitude for emergency navigation via instruments.

2) If you are communicating with ATC and in radar contact, ask the controller for a minimum safe altitude for your location and route of flight.

3) If you are not communicating with ATC, then attempt to contact them for the assistance above.

4) If you are unable to communicate with ATC or they do not have you on radar, you will need to determine a minimum safe altitude on your own.

   a) The first item that must be considered is the minimum altitude required for adequate terrain and obstacle clearance. This is of paramount importance.

      i) Determine your location.

      ii) Using your sectional chart, determine the Maximum Elevation Figure (MEF) for the chart quadrangle in which you are located or in which you intend to fly.

      iii) Add at least 1000 feet to the MEF to determine an adequate terrain and obstacle clearance altitude. A 2000 foot addition may be more appropriate in mountainous terrain.

   b) Next, you must determine the minimum altitude required for the navigational aids, communication services, and radar services to be used.

      i) VHF communications and navigation equipment requires line-of-site contact with a ground station.

      ii) Refer to the Airport/Facility Directory for the service class and any limitations to the reception of a particular VHF navigational ground station.

   c) The higher of the minimum altitude for adequate terrain and obstacle clearance and the minimum altitude for navigation and communication is your minimum safe altitude for emergency navigation via instruments.

Appendix G – Emergency and Survival Equipment

There are a number of emergency and survival products that may be available in your airplane. Items such as the Emergency Locator Transmitter are required by the regulations. Other products may include fire extinguishers, emergency floatation gear, equipment to protect you from the elements, or any number of other supplies. Regardless of the type of equipment on board, you should be familiar with its operation. Refer to the documentation supplied with the equipment for its operating instructions, servicing requirements, and safe storage methods.

The type of emergency and survival equipment you should carry will be highly dependent on the environment in which you will be flying. In general, you will want an aviation fire extinguisher and a small first aid kit onboard at all times. An emergency strobe light and flashlight with adequate batteries are also good to keep onboard. You should carry a mobile telephone with you while flying for use after an emergency landing. Review the lists below for a few environmentally influenced basics. Flying over remote locations may require additional equipment.

1) Cold weather
   a) Coats, hats, and gloves.
   b) Blankets.
2) Hot weather
   a) Water.
   b) Sun protection.
3) Over water
   a) Personal floatation device (inflatable is preferred).
   b) Inflatable raft and water for extended over water flights.

Appendix H – Instructor Certification for Private Pilot Knowledge Test

NOTE: The endorsement below is representative of that required by 14 CFR Section 61.35 and 61.103(d)(1) and (2) and **MUST** be made in the applicant's logbook.

INSTRUCTOR CERTIFICATION

PRIVATE PILOT KNOWLEDGE TEST

I certify I have reviewed the home study curriculum of (First name, MI, Last name) on the required training of § 61.105. I have determined he/she is prepared for the Private Pilot knowledge test.

Date: _____

Signed: _____

Certificate #: _____

Expires: _____